Kindness

A Pocket Guide

How it empowers health and success and why we need to prioritise it now

Sebastian Bóo

Illustrations by Leo Bonetto

Research contributions by Steven Cooney

First published in the UK by

K A P

Kindness Advantage Publishing
Managing Editor: Steven Cooney
Deputy Editor: Bonny Hazelwood
Editorial Assistance: Emily Pyle
Designer: Leo Bonetto

A CIP catalogue record for this book is available for the British
Library
ISBN 978-1-9169053-0-6
Typeset in Libre Caslon 11 pt

Kindness Advantage Publishing, a division of Kindness
Advantage Ltd.
8 Formby Court, Morgan Road, London N7 8NE
Kindness-advantage.com

Kindness Advantage™ is a registered trademark in the UK to
Kindness Advantage Ltd.

For all my amazing former, current and future students and for my nephews and niece: Felix, Clement, Albie, Felicity, Francisk, Nicolas and Luca.

Contents

List of Figures

Introduction

What wisdom can you find that is greater than kindness?
- Jean Jacques Rousseau

No act of kindness, no matter how small, is ever wasted.
- Aesop

This short book empowers you to be a kindness champion. It arms you with knowledge that will enable you to have greater influence and impact. You will be able to explain the many advantages of kindness, from improvements in physical and mental health to enhanced business success, leadership quality and better education and politics. You will be able to confidently counter claims that in certain contexts, kindness is unhelpful, encouraging over-dependence or impeding competitiveness, productivity and performance. When you have finished reading, you will be a more self-assured and stronger advocate for kindness, able to motivate and inspire others. You will achieve this, in great part, because you will be able to make the scientific, research-based, data-driven case for kindness.

The contents of this pocket guide are not sentimental, moralising or philosophical, but firmly grounded in research findings published in the peer-reviewed scientific literature. My academic training is in medical science, neuroscience, management and education. For over ten years, at the London School of Economics and at Birkbeck

College, University of London, I have been teaching students, among other things, how to analyse, evaluate and summarise research papers. Furthermore, since 2011, I have been following the developing research on kindness and compassion. My PhD research is on kindness in leadership and organisations. I have waded through hundreds of academic papers, read tens of books and attended numerous conferences so that you do not have to. This pocket guide is a concentrated distillate of all that research. Each chapter provides you, in summarised and simple form, expert-level knowledge directly from cutting-edge research. You do not need any background in science to read what follows, but should you want to look up the original research, each chapter is fully referenced.

The idea for this book came after I saw my thirty-year-old cousin and childhood playmate die from an inoperable brain tumour. This made me consider what will be going through my mind when I am on my own deathbed. I realised, that for me, it will be important to believe that I have contributed in some way to making the world better. So, "what does our world most need right now?" I asked myself. My answer was, and still is, "more kindness". This provides both the reason for and premise of this pocket guide. Kindness is still not sufficiently prioritised, and the world urgently needs more of it: not soft, let's-all-be-nice, submissive kindness, but intelligent, courageous, and fierce kindness. This means taking wise, and sometimes difficult, action to support wellbeing and reduce distress and suffering in others.

Many of us understand, intuitively, that kindness should be prioritised. The COVID-19 pandemic has emphasised how interconnected we are and how important it is to care, reach out and be kind.

Knowing how to engage in individual acts of kindness, towards people we meet or those close to us, is often simple enough. Knowing how we can *collectively* achieve a kinder society and world is not so clear. The plentiful evidence of a lack of kindness, from cyber bullying among children, domestic abuse, structural inequalities to wars, rather proves this point.

Our economic, political and social systems, as well as our media, do not always seem to help the cause for greater kindness on Planet Earth[1]. Their impacts reflect back to us beliefs, motivations and values, dominant in our history and the power structures of society. All of these ultimately stem from our complex human nature. It is obvious that human nature has a dark side[2]. We all have the capacity to be selfish, nasty and cruel. It is valid to point out here, that it is predominantly men, especially white men (an identity I share) that have, throughout history, done a supremely good job of demonstrating these darker aspects of human nature. Human nature also has a positive side. We can be capable of great kindness and compassion and it seems, taking a historical perspective, that we are getting a little less violent and cruel to each other[3&4]. The big question is, how do we further shift the needle of our human nature towards behaving with more kindness?

Removing obstacles to kindness is a big part of the answer; three such obstacles in particular. Firstly, a lack of awareness as to just how helpful prioritising kindness can be for solving the serious problems we face in many different arenas of life. Secondly, there still exist concerns that kindness is associated with weakness and therefore can get in the way of being competitive and successful. Thirdly, it can be difficult or impossible to be kind because perceptions, prejudices and environments conspire to effectively switch off our capacity for kindness, whilst simultaneously ramping up our tendency to not be kind.

The information in this pocket guide, in combination with your actions, can weaken these obstacles and facilitate the spread of kindness. This book helps you to tell others why it is important and urgent that we all take kindness more seriously and address what can be done to make it easier to be kind more often.

We start, in Chapter One, by clarifying what kindness is, and what it is not. In Chapter Two you learn about the neurobiological underpinnings of our capacity for kindness and unkindness. Next, Chapter Three explains the advantages kindness offers for physical health. In Chapter Four we discuss kindness in relation to mental health. Chapter Five focuses specifically on how kindness to oneself has advantages for wellbeing, resilience and our capacity to perform at our very best, particularly in high–stakes situations. Chapter Six considers what can be done to enhance kindness in the closest relationships we have with friends, family, partners and children. Chapter Seven considers the advantages of fostering kindness in education and how kindness helps the brain learn. Improving the performance of organisations and teams, and the quality of life of those working for organisations is the focus of Chapter Eight, which leads on to the discussion of the role of kindness in enhancing leadership of Chapter Nine. The challenges of promoting greater kindness and the risk that not-so-kind things are done under the pretence of being kind are discussed in Chapter Ten, which also considers the critiques and dangers of promoting kindness. We live in an ever more complex, interconnected world with constant innovation and technological developments, which, whilst they offer solutions to some existing challenges, also present great risks. How we can promote kindness at the societal level to help us tackle the problems we face, and the relevance of kindness for politics, our cities and the environment is discussed in Chapter Eleven. Finally, Chapter Twelve emphasises the urgency to take kindness seriously and to be strategic, smart and determined in bringing about an evolution of our minds and hearts.

The stakes are high. There are valid reasons to be pessimistic about the future. Researchers at the University of Oxford's Future of Humanity Institute predict we have at least a one in six chance of humanity destroying itself within the next one hundred years, through for example, a bioengineered pandemic or malign use of artificial intelligence[5&6].

Optimism for a safe and harmonious future on Planet Earth is directly proportional to the extent to which we can elevate and upgrade our collective capacity for kindness. The world needs us all to play a part in making this happen. You know kindness is important. That is why you are reading this right now. We need others to understand that making kindness a priority is intelligent and necessary. What is more, kindness makes you happier, healthier and more successful in both your relationships and your work.

So read this pocket guide. Internalise the content that makes sense to you and use it. Pass the information and the book on to others. Go out there and champion kindness!

References

[1] Gilbert, P. (2019) *Living Like Crazy.* York: Annwyn House.

[2] Staub, E. (1992). *The Roots of Evil: The Origins of Genocide and Other Group Violence*. Cambridge: CUP.

[3] Waal, F. de. (2019). *The Age of Empathy: Nature's Lessons for a Kinder Society*. London: Souvenir Press.

[4] Pinker, S. (2011). *The better angels of our nature: The decline of violence in history.* London: Penguin.

[5] Bostrom, N. (2019) *The Vulnerable World Hypothesis. Global Policy.* 10(4). 455-476. doi: 10.1111/1758-5899.12718.

[6] Ord, T. (2020) *The Precipice: Existential Risk and the Future of Humanity*: London: Bloomsbury.

Chapter 1
What is Kindness?

Three things in human life are important: the first is to be kind; the second is to be kind; and the third is to be kind. - Henry James

Kindness is a simple word. Everybody gets it. It is about being caring, understanding, considerate, helpful, attentive and nice, right? Well, yes, and no. Kindness does involve sensitivity and concern for others, but it does not always mean being nice. Some acts of kindness require courage and robust assertiveness, both of which may necessitate acting in ways that most people would not recognise as being nice. Here, I will define kindness and explain how it relates to other concepts, how human beings have evolved to be kind and how our capacity for kindness is turned on, or off.

Kindness involves doing something freely that is exclusively intended to promote wellbeing and/or reduce or prevent suffering. Kindness can flow in three ways: from you to another, from others to you and, as I discuss in Chapter Five, you can give and receive kindness to and from your own self.

To understand both the similarities and differences between kindness, empathy, sympathy and compassion, it helps to know there are three parts to kindness: the kind act itself; the intention behind the act; and the initial awareness that signalled a need, or opportunity, for kindness (see Fig. 1).

Fig. 1. Visual metaphor of the three parts of kindness

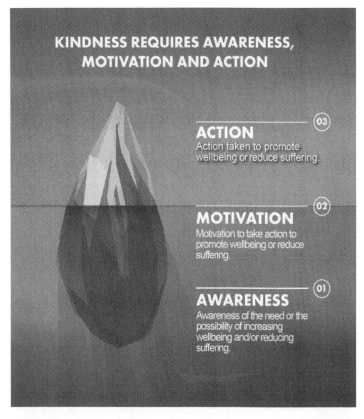

This initial awareness is what we call empathy. Empathy can range from being entirely feeling-based, to being entirely thinking-based[1&2]. Feeling-based, or affective, empathy means you experience the feelings of another person; you sense the sadness or joy of the other person in your own body. Thinking-based, or cognitive, empathy, means you intellectually understand somebody's circumstances by taking their perspective. We can exert some choice over how empathic we are in any given situation. Both feeling- and thinking-based empathy are skills which we can improve with practice[3&4]. While empathy can obviously facilitate being kind, empathy alone is not sufficient for kindness, as kindness requires action.

Sympathy is awareness of others' circumstances, specifically in the sense of sharing their feelings and commiserating with their distress, but, as with empathy, it does not require taking action.

Compassion is an awareness of suffering, coupled with the intention and action taken to relieve or prevent it[5]. What differentiates kindness from compassion is that, whilst compassion is solely focused on the prevention and relief of suffering, kindness is broader as it also encompasses action taken to promote wellbeing, which need not be a response to suffering. For instance, giving an elderly neighbour – who, as far as you know is well and not suffering – a gift to make her happy would be an act of kindness, but not one of compassion. If, however, you knew she was suffering a bereavement and you took the time to comfort her, this would be an example of compassion. Both acts are kind, but only the second is compassionate, as it concerns action that is based on an awareness of, and intention to address, suffering.

Recognising that kindness often includes compassion makes it easier to understand how being kind can be hard*. For example, entering a burning building to save a child would be an act of compassion as well as one of courage. Similarly, taking action to try to prevent a colleague suffering bullying at work would also be compassionate action and require assertiveness and some bravery, especially if the bully is your manager.

Most people, most of the time, want to be kind, but sometimes false beliefs about kindness hindering tough decision-making and success in business, management and competitive situations, stop people prioritising kindness. This aim of this pocket guide is to debunk these false beliefs! There is no evidence of a trade-off between kindness and success. On the contrary, the research indicates kindness facilitates success.

As human beings we are evolved for kindness, as kindness offered our ancestors advantages[6]. Firstly, the kindness of adults towards babies and youngsters helped to ensure they survived the inherent dangers of childhood and reached Secondly, we spent most of our evolutionary history living in tribes of about 150 people[7] and kindness, through facilitating relationships of sharing, trust and affection, served as the social glue that ensured such tribes were and remained cohesive functioning units. Finally, kindness is a highly attractive quality in a potential partner, as it signals the individual will care and devote resources to the partner and any future children[6&8].

* Paul Gilbert (5), founder of compassion focussed therapy, argues kindness is limited to actions that promote wellbeing and that it does not included actions to reduce suffering which are exclusively the domain of compassion. I have chosen, in line with psychologist Lee Rowland (11), to subsume compassion into the definition of kindness.

If humans evolved to be kind, why is it that people are, so often, not kind? Imagine we have a switch for kindness, one that turns kindness on and off. The presence or absence of empathy is the most significant factor involved in turning this switch on or off[9&10]. Empathy, in turn, is facilitated or inhibited by the extent to which we perceive others to be like us. The problem is that we are very good at quickly, and often subconsciously, identifying who is like us, and who is not like us[11], and subsequently creating stories to justify our perceptions of difference.

The good news is that we can train ourselves to identify and focus on the similarities between us and others, and empathy is a trainable skill[4]. Thus, we can get better at kindness. Drawing upon recent research, the following chapters make the case that being kinder advantages us in our physical and mental health, our relationships with others and our own selves, and our ability to lead. We will also learn how kindness advantages organisational performance, education and learning, as well as underpins much needed changes in how we do our politics, run our cities and treat the environment.

At an intuitive level, we often sense that our capacity for kindness is related to the heart. Indeed, many of us feel a warmth in our chest when we experience kindness and as you will learn in Chapter Three, kindness is indeed good for the health of your heart. Scientific research on the role of the human heart and kindness, and the connection between the brain and the heart in relation to human emotions[12] has begun but is in its infancy. At present, the role of the brain in generating either kindness or a lack of kindness is becoming better understood. Therefore, before finding about how we benefit from the positive power of kindness, the next chapter explains the brain's role in kindness.

References

[1] Cuff, B. M., Brown, S. J., Taylor, L. & Howat, D. J. (2016). Empathy: A review of the concept. *Emotion Review*, *8*(2), 144-153. doi: 10.1177/1754073914558466.

[2] Baron-Cohen, S. (2011). *Zero degrees of empathy: A new theory of human cruelty*. London: Penguin.

[3] Zaki, J. (2020). *The war for kindness: Building empathy in a fractured world*. New York: Broadway Books.

[4] Zaki, J. (2014). Empathy: a motivated account. *Psychological Bulletin*, *140*(6), 1608-1647. doi: 10.1037/a0037679.

[5] Gilbert, P. (Ed.). (2005). *Compassion: Conceptualisations, research and use in psychotherapy*. London: Routledge.

[6] Keltner, D., Marsh, J. & Smith, J. A. (Eds.). (2010). *The compassionate instinct: The science of human goodness*. New York: Norton & Company.

[7] Dunbar, R. (2010). *How many friends does one person need?: Dunbar's number and other evolutionary quirks*. London: Faber & Faber.

[8] Spikins, P. (2015). *How compassion made us human: The evolutionary origins of tenderness, trust and morality*. London: Pen and Sword.

[9] Molenberghs, P. (2013). The neuroscience of in-group bias. *Neuroscience & Biobehavioral Reviews*, *37*(8), 1530-1536. doi: 10.1016/j.neubiorev.2013.06.002.

[10] Miller, M. (2019). Emotional Rescue: The Heart-Brian Connection, *In Cerebrum: the Dana Forum on Brain Science* (2019) Vol. 2019, May-Jun 2019. Dana Foundation.

[11] Rowland, L. (2018). Kindness: Society's golden chain. *The Psychologist*, 31, 30-35.

[12] Di Bello, M., Carnevali, L., Petrocchi, N., Thayer, J. F3., Gilbert, P., & Ottaviani, C. (2020). The compassionate vagus: a meta-analysis on the connection between compassion and heart rate variability. *Neuroscience & Biobehavioral Reviews. 116*, 21-30 doi: 10.1016/j.neubiorev.2020.06.016.

Chapter 2
The Neurobiology of Kindness

The brain is the organ of destiny. It holds within its humming mechanism secrets that will determine the future of the human race. - Dr Wilder Penfield, pioneering neurosurgeon

Our human brains have evolved over thousands of years and come with a number of built-in features: think of them as pre-installed apps on a smartphone that cannot be deleted. These apps helped our ancestors survive and some of them predispose us to being kind and happy, whilst others predispose us to being nasty and depressed. The human brain is amazing and wonderful, but also problematic and tricky. We have both an evolutionarily old part of the brain and a more recently evolved part, as well as three emotional regulation systems: a threat, a drive and a soothing system[1,2,3&4]. Understanding our brain and these three emotional regulation systems enables us to manage our emotions better and train ourselves to benefit more from kindness. This approach has been developed by Professor Paul Gilbert and is the basis of Compassion Focused Therapy, now being applied beyond the therapy room to education, healthcare and business[1].

The first emotional regulation system, our threat system, belongs to the evolutionarily older part of the brain involving the right and left amygdala, located in the middle of your brain at the level of your ears[5] (see Fig. 2). The threat system responds to dangers and prepares our body for fight or flight by activating our sympathetic nervous system. This triggers the release of noradrenaline and cortisol, leading to changes in our body such as increased heart rate, reduced blood flow to our gut and increased blood flow to our legs. During the process we can feel fear, anxiety or anger. Although the threat system evolved to help us, it can become over-active and respond to imaginary threats, which, if this occurs excessively, can leave us mentally unwell and exhausted.

Fig. 2. Structures of the brain when cut vertically though the midline (sagittal plane)

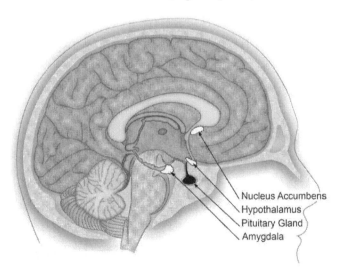

Nucleus Accumbens
Hypothalamus
Pituitary Gland
Amygdala

Furthermore, when our threat system is active, kindness is not a priority. Unfortunately, a number of our brain apps make it easy for the threat system to become over-active. These apps include the negativity bias, whereby we overestimate threats and preferentially focus on the bad or what may go wrong[6&7]. Another app ensures we quickly distinguish between in-group and out-group members[8]. In-group members are people with whom we feel safe and share a sense of belonging. Out-group members are people towards whom we feel no affinity. Our brain's default response to them is threat system activation.

There is also our social comparison app, which fires up our threat system whenever we feel inferior through comparing ourselves to others[9]. Our ability to think about ourselves, to have a self-concept, to imagine what might happen to us in the future, to ruminate on what has happened in the past are all features of the much more recently evolved part of the brain. These newer brain features can interact with the threat system, the older evolved part of the brain, in unhelpful ways, leading to threat system activation and anxiety. This happens, for example, when we imagine how things might not work out for us in the future, or when ruminating over something that went wrong in the past.

A further design feature of the brain, we need to understand, is that we have two thinking modes: an active thinking mode and a passive, mind-wandering, mode[10].

The neural circuitry for the passive, mind-wandering, mode has been identified and named the default mode network[11] (see Fig. 3). On average, people spend 80 per cent of their waking day in this mode[12].

When we are in mind-wandering mode, i.e. not thinking actively, our various brain apps feed our thought stream. Sometimes these automatic thoughts will lead to pleasant emotional responses. Other times they will cause either neutral or distressing emotional responses. For example, the social comparison app causes us to have thoughts related to how we believe we compare to others. On some occasions, we will have thoughts comparing ourselves favourably, generating positive feelings. On other occasions, we will make unfavourable comparisons between ourselves and others, who we perceive are better than us, leading to distressing feelings. The human brain's negativity bias ensures that it is the thoughts that induce distressing feelings that are more likely to occur. A constant trickle of negative thoughts, activating the threat system, puts us at risk of anxiety and depression.

The second emotional regulation system, the drive system, gives us motivation to acquire everything we need to progress in life: from food, shelter and friends, to sex, status and success[1&3]. The drive system involves a region of the brain known as the brain's pleasure centre: the nucleus accumbens (see Fig. 2). The neurotransmitter dopamine is released within the nucleus accumbens when you get what you want, making you feel good and also giving you the motivation to get more of the same[13].

Fig. 3. The default mode network (sagittal plane)

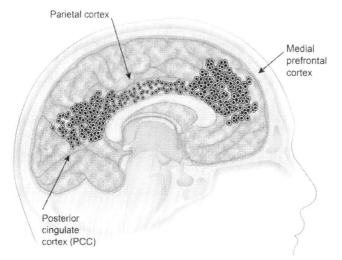

The brain's default mode network is active when we are engaged in mind-wandering. It consists of several interconnected regions including the posterior cingulate cortex, the medial prefrontal cortex & parietal cortex.

The drive and the threat systems can feed off each other in unhelpful ways. Somebody whose threat system is activated by, for example, self-critical thoughts, may seek pleasure to override the distressing feelings but the pleasure only temporarily mask the distress. Furthermore, over time, ever more drive system activation is required to produce the same level of positive feelings. In this way, people can end up caught on a hedonic treadmill constantly seeking and chasing the next ever-bigger, ever-greater success or pleasure, without this ever being enough for them[14]. If people cannot get what they want, their threat system can become yet further activated. This pattern of thought and behaviour, in its extreme form, leads to addiction.

Finally, the third emotional regulation system, is the soothing system, which counteracts the effects of the drive and threat systems. It activates when we are content and safe, making us feel good, warm and at peace. The soothing system is important in sustaining relationships of trust and affection, as well as for regulating our own selves emotionally. It involves the release of endorphins and oxytocin, made in the brain's pituitary gland (see Fig. 2) as well as through activation of the vagus nerve (see Fig. 4), causing a slowing down of the heart rate and a slight lengthening of the out-breath, serving to calm us down. Our soothing system is activated when we receive genuine kindness from others, enabling us to generate kind thoughts and be kind more easily. We need much more of this!

Our world, with its 24-hour news, non-stop social media and advertising, and the predominance of a politics of discord, increasing wealth and social inequalities means that there is so much in our environment to stimulate the threat and drive systems and very little to trigger our soothing system; all more apparent and accentuated by the COVID-19 pandemic. Continual over-activation of the threat and drive systems, along with long-term inhibition of our soothing system, limits our capacity for kindness.

The world we have created reflects back to us the working of our brains. It is not our fault that the human brain is tricky[1], but if we want a better world, a kinder world, we need to become more aware of the nature of our brain. Armed with a scientifically- informed understanding of the brain, we can, and must, take action now. As individuals, communities and societies, we must create environments that will tame our threat and drive systems, boost our soothing system and facilitate our innate capacity for kindness.

We must apply the science of kindness, and our improved understanding of our human brains to facilitate kindness and "design for kindness". This means we must plan, organise and structure the way we run our organisations, our businesses, our society and ultimately our world, so that being kind is prioritised, rewarded and celebrated. We know a lot about what can be done to nurture both our individual and societal capacity for kindness and thus create a world which reflects this. Now we must just do it.

An understanding of how kindness can solve the problems we presently face can help to generate the political will and personal motivation to champion kindness and take concrete action. In the next chapter, you will learn how kindness can help improve your cognitive performance, as well as reduce and prevent mental illness. Mental illness affects one in four people in the UK[15], one in five in the USA[16], and represents 22 per cent of the overall burden, worldwide, caused by all diseases and disabilities[17].

Fig. 4. The vagus nerves

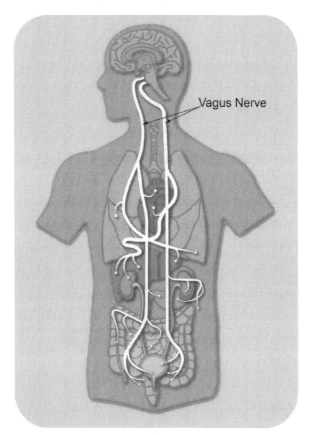

References

[1] Gilbert, P. (2014). The origins and nature of compassion focused therapy. *British Journal of Clinical Psychology, 53*(1), 6-41. doi: 10.1111/bjc.12043.

[2] Panksepp, J., Lane, R. D., Solms, M. & Smith, R. (2017). Reconciling cognitive and affective neuroscience perspectives on the brain basis of emotional experience. *Neuroscience & Biobehavioral Reviews*, *76*, 187-215. doi: 10.1016/j.neubiorev.2016.09.010.

[3] Panksepp, J. (2010). Affective neuroscience of the emotional BrainMind: evolutionary perspectives and implications for understanding depression. *Dialogues in clinical neuroscience*, *12*(4), 533. doi: 10.31887/DCNS.2010.12.4/jpanksepp.

[4] Depue, R. A., & Morrone-Strupinsky, J. V. (2005). A neurobehavioral model of affiliative bonding: Implications for conceptualizing a human trait of affiliation. *Behavioral and Brain Sciences*, *28*(3), 313-349. doi: 10.1017/S0140525X05420063.

[5] Bishop, S. J. (2008). Neural mechanisms underlying selective attention to threat. *Annals of the New York Academy of Sciences*, *1129*(1), 141-152. doi: 10.1196/annals.1417.016.

[6] Baumeister, R. F., Bratslavsky, E., Finkenauer, C. & Vohs, K. D. (2001). Bad is stronger than good. *Review of general psychology*, *5*(4), 323-370. doi: 10.1037/1089-2680.5.4.323.

[7] Rozin, P. & Royzman, E. B. (2001). Negativity bias, negativity dominance, and contagion. *Personality and social psychology review*, *5*(4), 296-320. doi: 10.1207/S15327957PSPR0504_2.

[8] Morrison, S., Decety, J. & Moldenbrghs, P. (2012). The neuroscience of group membership. *Neuropsychogia*, *50*(8), 2114-2120. doi: 10.1016/j.neuropsychogia.2012.05.014.

[9] Swencionis, J. K. & Fiske, S. T. (2014). How social neuroscience can inform theories of social comparison. *Neuropsychologia*, *56*, 140-146. doi: 10.1016/j.neuropsychologia.2014.01.009.

[10] Mason, M. F., Norton, M. I., Van Horn, J. D., Wegner, D. M., Grafton, S. T. & Macrae, C. N. (2007). Wandering minds: the default network and stimulus-independent thought. *Science*, *315*(5810), 393-395. doi: 10.1126/science.1131295.

[11] Raichle, M. E. (2015). The brain's default mode network. *Annual review of neuroscience*, *38*, 433-447. doi: 10.1146/annurev-neuro-071013-014030.

[12] Killingsworth, M. A. & Gilbert, D. T. (2010). A wandering mind is an unhappy mind. *Science*, *330*(6006), 932-932. doi: 10.1126/science.1192439.

[13] Kringelbach, M. L. & Berridge, K. C. (2016). 'Neuroscience of reward, motivation and drive'. In, Kim, S. I., Reeve, J. & Bong, M. (eds.) *Advances in Motivation & Achievement: Recent Developments in Neuroscience Research on Human Motivation,* Bingley: Emerald Group Publishing. 23-35.

[14] Bottan, L. & Truglia, P. (2011). Deconstructing the hedonic treadmill: Is happiness autoregressive?. *The Journal of Socio-Economics*, *40*(3), 224-236. doi: 10.1016/j.socec.2011.01.007.

[15] McManus, S., Bebbington, P., Jenkins, R. & Brugha. T. (eds.) (2016). Mental health & wellbeing in England: Adult psychiatric morbidity survey 2014. NHS Digital. Available at https://webarchive.nationalarchives.gov.uk/20180328140249/http://digitial.nhs.uk/catalogue/PUB21748 [Accessed 12-06-21].

[16] U.S. Department of Health & Human Services (HHS), Substance Abuse & Mental Health Services Administration (2020). *Key Substance Use & Mental Health Indicators: Results from the 2020 National Survey.* Available at https://www.samhsa.gov/data/report/national-survey-substance-abuse-treatment-services-n-ssats-2020-data-substance-abuse [Accessed 12-06-21].

[17] World Health Organization. (2016). *Disease burden estimates for 2000-2015.* Available at http://www.who.int/healthinfo/global_burden_disease/esti mates/en/index2.html [Accessed 12-06-21].

Chapter 3

Kindness for Mental Health and Performance

People who are kind and compassionate see clear
benefits to their wellbeing and happiness. -
Mark Rowland, CEO Mental Health UK

The highest form of wisdom is kindness. - *The Talmud*

Rizwan, known to his friends as Riz, is at an
interview, about to face a panel of four partners at a
law firm who will determine whether he is offered
the job. He knows there is strong competition and
he might not get the offer he wants. Not getting
what we want, or feel we need, is interpreted as a
threat by our brain. The thought of failing the
interview activates Riz's emotional threat system,
making him feel anxious. To reduce the negative
impact of the anxiety on his ability to perform at his
very best, Riz uses a kindness-based technique to
hack his neurobiology and calm himself down
before the interview properly begins. He knows it
is impossible for his brain to think kind thoughts
towards the interviewers and simultaneously
perceive them, or the situation, as threatening. To
trick his brain into generating kind and
compassionate thoughts towards the interviewers,
not something he would naturally do in such a
situation, he quickly imagines possible sources of

distress and pain in the interviewers' lives: perhaps the man with the green tie has an elderly parent who is severely ill and perhaps the woman with the red-rimmed glasses is worried about her child.

These thoughts shift his perception of the interviewers. They no longer feel quite as threatening and he is aware of a slight sense of warmth towards them. These are not dominant thoughts or feelings as Riz is still very much alert and focused on performing at his best. However, with the slight reduction in the activation of his threat system, he does feel a better, friendlier and kinder connection with his potential future employers. This makes him feel more confident, bold and strong. He is calmer too. His voice softens, he smiles more naturally, his body language becomes more fluid and he appears self-assured, calm and collected. "Way to go, mate!" Riz thinks to himself, as he knows he has given a good first impression. When the woman with the glasses throws Riz a difficult curveball question, his lack of excessive nerves means he is more creative and mentally nimble in constructing an answer that impresses.

Oxytocin, a neuropeptide, is released from a part of the brain called the posterior pituitary and is involved in the neurobiology of kindness, amongst other things[1,2&3]. When you connect with others and develop rapport, that warm, good feeling of trusted safe human connection is mediated, in great part, by oxytocin[3]. Oxytocin dampens down activation of the amygdalae, which are the central hubs of the brain's fear and anxiety circuitry[4]. When in a threat state your amygdalae are activated, causing the part of the brain called the prefrontal cortex to go off-line[5]. This means that, when you feel excessively anxious, you cannot think straight or make level-headed decisions[6]. Oxytocin, by toning down the reactivity of the amygdalae[4] and thus dampening your emotional fear and threat system, helps ensure your prefrontal cortex remains fully online.

In the example with Riz, generating kind thoughts towards the interviewers interrupts the normal threat response and promotes a greater sense of connection. This helps Riz benefit from the positive effects of oxytocin on both his emotional state and his cognitive performance. Many of my clients have reported the effectiveness of the kind thoughts technique to feel less anxious, more confident and perform better in difficult and high-stakes situations, such as Harvard MBA selection interviews and medical consultant job interviews.

Feeling anxious in certain situations is normal, of course. It is only if the anxiety has a negative impact on our performance that it requires addressing. It is also a problem, if one experiences excessive anxiety, depression, or other distressing emotions, such as anger, frequently, and in a way that seems disproportionate to our life events. Every year, one in four of us will be affected by poor mental health or mental illness[7]. We will certainly all have family, friends and colleagues who experience poor mental health or mental illness. Poor mental health and mental illness causes suffering, relationships to break down[8,] lost productivity at work[9] and significantly increases the chances of being physically ill[10]. According to a 2020 report by Deloitte, the economic cost of poor mental health to UK employers was £45 billion in 2017, representing a rise of 16 per cent from the previous year[11]. Who knows how much this figure will have risen due to the challenges of COVID-19? No individual or organisation can afford *not* to take action to protect and promote mental health.

Prioritising kindness promotes good mental health and prevents and relieves mental illness[12]. Let us clarify what we mean by mental health and how it differs from mental illness. Mental illness means having a diagnosable condition like depression, anxiety or schizophrenia. A person can have a mental illness but, by managing themselves well, they may be able to experience good mental health, just as somebody with a physical illness, such as diabetes, can still be physically healthy[13]. Our mental health relates to the ongoing stream of thoughts and emotions we experience over time, and the extent to which the habits in our thoughts, and patterns in our emotions, either help or hinder us in living healthy lives.

Imagine that your mental health is your inner weather[14]. Your inner weather is affected by the outer weather of events and circumstances of your life, but you can also regulate your inner weather. Having good mental health means you are able to use and regulate your thoughts and emotions in ways that help you both cope with challenge and pursue your goals effectively. Furthermore, good mental health allows you to enjoy the positive emotions associated with relationships and achievements[13]. Good mental health supports us in coping with, and succeeding in life, no matter how we choose to define success. And just as we can work on our physical health to become fitter, we can also do things to optimise our mental health and wellbeing.

A critical first step in the process of improving mental health is developing awareness of our thoughts and emotions, and how we respond to them[15]. The thoughts and emotions we have are influenced by the interpretations and meanings we give to events in our lives and how we think about the future. In other words, what we think and say to ourselves, our attitudes and self-talk, influence our emotions and subsequent thoughts. By becoming aware of, and taking charge of, our attitudes and self-talk, and exercising flexibility in querying and modifying our own thoughts, perspectives and narratives, we can do a lot to brighten our inner weather[16]. If we inject kindness into the way we perform these mental processes, there is a powerful positive impact on our mental health, as we will cover further, when discussing self-kindness, in Chapter Five.

When kind thoughts manifest in kind action, the advantages for mental health are magnified, as evidenced by numerous studies[12&17]. The beneficial effects of kindness occur, because giving or receiving kindness is associated with thoughts, perspectives and inner dialogues that both reduce emotional threat system activation and boost soothing system activation[18]. For example, when we are kind to others, it diverts our attention away from the self onto the other person. With this shift, any negative self-referential thinking no longer holds our attention. This explains why individuals with high levels of social anxiety who commit to regularly undertaking kind acts experience a significant improvement in positive emotion and a decrease in their level of social avoidance[19]. The reduction in threat system activation, induced by kindness, means less frequent feelings of anxiety, fear, irritation and frustration[18]. Conversely, the increase in soothing system activation, as a result of giving or receiving kindness, produces feelings of being calm, safe, satisfied and at peace[18]. When we are kind to others, we can also experience the reward of meeting our human needs for social connection, belonging and having purpose. Similarly, when others are kind to us, it usually meets our need for feeling we belong and that we are significant[20]. So, kindness serves to regulate our emotional systems in ways that support mental health[12]. As was the case with Riz, kindness in thoughts and actions also supports mental performance, by reducing the detrimental impact of anxiety on working memory, cognitive flexibility and creative problem-solving[21].

Improving our mental health not only reduces our risk of mental illness, but also enhances our capacity to thrive, succeed and fulfil our potential. Improving our mental health enables us to cope better with adversity, as well as develop the inner resources of courage, self-nurturance and determination, that we need in order to take on the challenges we must actively seek out to achieve our goals[13]. Furthermore, good mental health helps us to love, which is ultimately what makes our lives most worth living. Improving our mental health by harnessing the power of kindness is therefore something we should all be doing.

References

[1] MacDonald, K. & MacDonald, T. M. (2010). The peptide that binds: a systematic review of oxytocin and its prosocial effects in humans. *Harvard review of psychiatry*, *18*(1), 1-21. doi: 10.3109/10673220903523615.

[2] Neff, K. D. (2012). The science of self-compassion. In Germer, C. & Siegel, R. (Eds) *Compassion and wisdom in psychotherapy*, Guildford: Guildford Press, pp 79-92.

[3] Saturn, S. R. (2017). Two factors that fuel compassion: The oxytocin system and the social experience of moral elevation In Seppälä, E., et al., (Eds). *Oxford handbook of compassion science*, 121-132. doi: 10.1093/oxfordhb/9780190464684.013.10.

[4] Kirsch, P., Esslinger, C., Chen, Q., Mier, D., Lis, S., Siddhanti, S., Gruuppe, H., Mattay, S. M., Gallhofer, B. & Meyer-Lindenberg, A. (2005). Oxytocin modulates neural circuitry for social cognition and fear in humans. *Journal of neuroscience*, *25*(49), 11489-11493. doi: 10.1523/JNEUROSCI.3984-05.2005.

[5] Bishop, S., Duncan, J., Brett, M. & Lawrence, A. D. (2004). Prefrontal cortical function and anxiety: controlling attention to threat-related stimuli. *Nature neuroscience*, *7*(2), 184-188. doi: 10.1038/nn1173.

[6] Yang, Z., Saini, R. & Freling, T. (2015). How anxiety leads to suboptimal decisions under risky choice situations. *Risk analysis*, *35*(10), 1789-1800. doi: 10.1111/risa.12343.

[7] McManus, S., Meltzer, H., Brugha, T. S., Bebbington, P. E. & Jenkins, R. (2009). Adult psychiatric morbidity in

England, 2007: results of a household survey. The NHS Information Centre for health and social care.

[8] Monson, C. M., Taft, C. T. & Fredman, S. J. (2009). Military-related PTSD and intimate relationships: From description to theory-driven research and intervention development. *Clinical psychology review*, *29*(8), 707-714. doi: 10.1016/j.cpr.2009.09.002.

[9] Bubonya, M., Cobb-Clark, D. A. & Wooden, M. (2017). Mental health and productivity at work: Does what you do matter?. *Labour economics*, 46, 150-165. doi: 10.1016/j.labeco.2017.05.001.

[10] Ohrnberger, J., Fichera, E. & Sutton, M. (2017). The relationship between physical and mental health: A mediation analysis. *Social Science & Medicine*, 195, 42-49. doi: 10.1016/j.socscimed.2017.11.008.

[11] Deloitte (2020). Mental Health and Employers. Refreshing the Case For Investment. Available at https://www2.deloitte.com/uk/en/pages/consulting/articles/mental-health-and-employers-refreshing-the-case-for-investment.html [Accessed 19-06-21].

[12] Curry, O. S., Rowland, L., Zlotowitz, S., McAlaney, J. & Whitehouse, H. (2018). Happy to Help. *A systematic review and meta-analysis of the effects of performing acts of kindness on the well-being of the actor. Journal of Experimental Social Psychology. 76,*320-329*.* doi: 10.1016/j.jesp.2018.02.014.

[13] Westerhof, G. J. & Keyes, C. L. (2010). Mental Illness and Mental Health: The Two Continua Model Across the Lifespan. *Journal of Adult Development*, 17(2), 110-119. doi: 10.1007/s10804-009-9082-y.

[14] Simm, A. (2020) personal communication, 12th June, 2020.

[15] Janssen, M., Heerkens, Y., Kuijer, W., Van Der Heijden, B. & Engels, J. (2018). Effects of Mindfulness-Based Stress

Reduction on employees' mental health: A systematic review. *PloS one*, 13(1), e0191332. doi: 10.1371/journal.pone.0191332.

[16] Johnson, E. A. & O'Brien, K. A. (2013). Self-compassion soothes the savage ego-threat system: Effects on negative affect, shame, rumination, and depressive symptoms. *Journal of Social and Clinical Psychology*, *32*(9), 939-963. doi: 10.1521/jscp.2013.32.9.939.

[17] Raposa, E. B., Laws, H. B. & Ansell, E. B. (2016). Prosocial behavior mitigates the negative effects of stress in everyday life. *Clinical Psychological Science*, *4*(4), 691-698. doi: 10.1177/2167702615611073.

[18] Gilbert, P. (2014). The origins and nature of compassion focused therapy. *British Journal of Clinical Psychology*, *53*(1), 6-41. doi: 10.1111/bjc.12043.

[19] Alden, L. E. & Trew, J. L. (2013). If it makes you happy: Engaging in kind acts increases positive affect in socially anxious individuals. *Emotion*, *13*(1), 64. doi: 10.1037/a0027761.

[20] Davis, M. H. (2018). Social Relationship & Social Behaviour. In *Empathy: A social psychological approach*, (p 120-150). New York: Routledge.

[21] Moran, T. P. (2016). Anxiety and working memory capacity: A meta-analysis and narrative review. *Psychological Bulletin*, *142*(8), 831. doi: 10.1037/bul0000051.

Chapter 4
Kindness for Health

Acts of kindness make us happier and healthier: they relieve the symptoms of depression and they even help us live longer, healthier lives. - *Dr David Hamilton*

Our social connections to others have powerful influences on health and longevity. - *Professor Julianne Holt-Lunstad*

If there were a drug that improved the health of the heart and blood vessels, boosted immunity, slowed down aging, and reduced pain and inflammation leading to a decreased risk of diabetes, arthritis and Alzheimer's, there would be huge demand for such a drug. Kindness has just these effects. Over forty years' worth of research has evidenced the beneficial associations between regularly engaging in kind and charitable behaviour and health[1&2]. Studies have shown that being kind through volunteering is associated with reduced blood pressure[3], reduced blood cholesterol[4], reduced blood glucose[4], less disease and longer, healthier lives[5]. These effects are independent of the other potential benefits of volunteering, such as exercise. Studies have demonstrated that just being kind, by donating money or writing a supportive note to a friend, reduces the harmful effects of excessive stress on the body[6].

It is not just being kind to others that boosts health. Practising self-kindness by, for example, speaking to oneself with a supportive inner voice, reduces long-term blood sugar levels in diabetic patients[7], and reduces both stress and biological markers of inflammation in university students taking exams[8].

Generating kind thoughts about other people, as is done repeatedly in loving kindness meditation, has been shown, in a randomised control trial, to reduce back pain[9] and improve cardiovascular function[10]. Loving kindness meditation has also been shown, by researchers at Harvard University, to be associated with healthier and younger cells in which genes and DNA are better protected from the damaging effects of ageing[11], thus demonstrating potential implications for protection against cancer. Human biology is so responsive to kindness, that even watching a video of others being kind boosts antibody levels, thus helping to strengthen immunity[12].

Kindness achieves all these positive health benefits by reducing activation of the threat emotional system and increasing activation of the soothing system, making us calmer and, as it turns out, healthier. Specifically, there is both a change in the activity of a long nerve called the vagus nerve (see Fig. 4) and increased release of oxytocin. Together these improve cardiovascular function and enhance immunity. It also leads to reduced inflammation and oxidative stress, which are key factors in causing many diseases. When we are kind, or receive kindness, the vagus nerve also causes a number of slight changes to our biology. These changes make it yet easier to connect and be kind to others. Professor Steven Porges describes all these slight changes in our biology, initiated by kindness, and controlled by the different branches of vagus nerve, as the social engagement system, because they help us to engage better with others[13].

One example of such a change is that when we receive or give kindness changes to the stimulation of certain muscles in our face occur. These facilitate eye contact and synchrony of facial expressions with another person, strengthening empathy and rapport. Another example is tiny muscles in our middle ears are activated, making it easier to ignore distracting noises and enabling us to better hear the voice of the other person. Furthermore, changes in the muscles in the larynx, our voice box, make it easier to speak with a softer voice tone[14]. Finally, and most significantly, the vagus acts as a brake on the heart rate, slowing it down, which helps us to be calmer, making it easier to reassure and soothe others[13&14]. The vagus also affects the pattern of the heartbeat, making the heartbeat slightly faster during inhalation and slightly slower during exhalation. This small variation in heart rate optimises the cardiovascular system, conserves energy, and is associated with stamina, physical and cognitive performance, longevity, and recovery from heart disease.

The vagus can also reduce inflammation[16]. When the sensory endings of the vagus nerve detect excessive inflammation in the body, the nerve initiates changes leading to a reduction in inflammation. These changes include increased cortisol secretion and reduced release of pro-inflammatory cytokines. Inflammation contributes to the disease process of nearly all chronic and degenerative conditions. Therefore, patients with chronic or degenerative conditions could particularly benefit from the vagus' ability to decrease inflammation[18].

Release of the neuropeptide oxytocin, from the posterior pituitary in the brain, is the second key mechanism that contributes to the beneficial impact of kindness on health[19]. Oxytocin is important in pregnancy and maternal behaviour, but also plays a broader biological role for both men and women. Like the vagus, oxytocin facilitates kind human interaction, by helping improve attention paid to others' faces. It achieves this by calming down the parts of the brain responsible for threat processing and increasing activity in the parts that respond to positive social opportunities[20&21]. Oxytocin's two key health promoting effects are that it reduces blood pressure[22] and enhances immunity[23].

Oxytocin reduces blood pressure by causing a slight dilation in the arteries, including those that supply the heart. Given that high blood pressure is a major risk factor for heart disease, oxytocin and, by extension, kindness protects the heart. Oxytocin also has antimicrobial effects, improving wound healing, as well as reducing oxidative stress[24&25] which, combined with inflammation, plays a significant role in many disease processes, including in the build-up of plaques on artery walls and in neurodegenerative diseases, such as Alzheimer's and Parkinson's[26].

Whether it is being kind to others, or being kind to ourselves, or others being kind to us, or watching others either be kind or receive kindness, our biology responds in ways that can have significant health benefits. Of course, we should not be kind simply because it is good for our health. We should be kind because it is morally the right thing to do, but perhaps knowing the health advantages of kindness, can give us a slight nudge or incentive, to both be on the lookout for opportunities for kindness and then to act on them.

References

[1] Detollenaere, J., Willems, S. & Baert, S. (2017). Volunteering, income and health. *PloS one*, 12(3), e0173139. doi: 10.1371/journal.pone.0173139.

[2] Jenkinson, C. E., Dickens, A. P., & Richards, S. H. (2013). Is volunteering a public health intervention? A systematic review and meta-analysis of the health and survival of volunteers. *BMC public health*, 13(1), 773. doi: 10.1186/1471-2458-13-773.

[3] Whillans, A. V., Dunn, E. W., Sandstrom, G. M., Dickerson, S. S. & Madden, K. M. (2016). Is spending money on others good for your heart? *Health Psychology: Official Journal of the Division of Health Psychology, American Psychological Association*, 35(6), 574–583. doi: 10.1037/hea0000332.

[4] Burr, J. A., Han, S. H. & Tavares, J. L. (2015). Volunteering and cardiovascular disease risk: Does helping others get "under the skin?". *The Gerontologist*, 56(5), 937-947. doi: 10.1093/geront/gnv032.

[5] Poulin, M. J. & Holman, E. A. (2013). Helping hands, healthy body? Oxytocin receptor gene and prosocial behavior interact to buffer the association between stress & physical health. *Hormones and Behavior*, 63(3), 510–517. doi: 10.1016/j.yhbeh.2013.01.004.

[6] Inagaki, T. K. (2018). Neural mechanisms of the link between giving social support and health. *Annals of the New York Academy of Science*. 1428, 33–50. doi: 10.1111/nyas.13703.

[7] Friis, A. M., Johnson, M. H., Cutfield, R. G. & Consedine, N. S. (2016). Kindness Matters: A Randomized Controlled Trial of a Mindful Self-Compassion Intervention Improves Depression, Distress, and HbA1c Among Patients With Diabetes. *Diabetes Care*, dc160416. doi: 10.2337/dc16-0416.

[8] Arch, J. J., Brown, K. W., Dean, D. J., Landy, L. N., Brown, K. D. & Laudenslager, M. L. (2014). Self-compassion training modulates alpha-amylase, heart rate variability, & subjective responses to social evaluative threat in women. *Psychoneuroendocrinology*, 49–58. doi: 10.1016/j.psyneuen.2013.12.018.

[9] Carson, J. W., Keefe, F. J., Lynch, T. R., Carson, K. M., Goli, V., Fras, A. M. & Thorp, S. R. (2005). Loving-kindness meditation for chronic low back pain: results from a pilot trial. *Journal of Holistic Nursing: Official Journal of the American Holistic Nurses' Association*, *23*(3), 287–304. doi: 10.1177/0898010105277651.

[10] Kok, B. E. & Fredrickson, B. L. (2010). Upward spirals of the heart: Autonomic flexibility, as indexed by vagal tone, reciprocally & prospectively predicts positive emotions & social connectedness. *Biological Psychology*, 85(3), 432–436. doi: 10.1016/j.biopsycho.2010.09.005.

[11] Hoge, E. A., Chen, M. M., & Simon, N. M. (2013). Loving-Kindness Meditation practice associated with longer telomeres in women. *Brain, Behavior, and Immunity*, 32, 159–163. doi: 10.1016/j.bbi.2013.04.005.

[12] McClelland, D. C. & Kirshnit, C. (1988). The effect of motivational arousal through films on salivary immunoglobulin A. *Psychology & Health*, *2*(1), 31–52. doi: 10.1080/08870448808400343.

[13] Porges, S. W. (2007). The polyvagal perspective. *Biological psychology*, 74(2), 116-143. doi: 10.1016/j.biopsycho.2006.06.009.

[14] Porges, S. W. (2001). The polyvagal theory: phylogenetic substrates of a social nervous system. *International journal of psychophysiology*, 42(2), 123-146. doi: 10.1016/s0167-8760(01)00162-3.

[15] Park, G. & Thayer, J. F. (2014). From the heart to the mind: cardiac vagal tone modulates top-down and bottom-up visual perception and attention to emotional stimuli. *Frontiers in Psychology*, 5. doi: 10.3389/fpsyg.2014.00278.

[16] Pavlov, V. A. & Tracey, K. J. (2017). Neural regulation of immunity: molecular mechanisms and clinical translation. *Nature neuroscience*, 20(2), 156. doi: 10.1038/nn.4477.

[17] O'Connor, J. C., McCusker, R. H., Strle, K., Johnson, R. W., Dantzer, R. & Kelley, K. W. (2008). Regulation of IGF-I function by proinflammatory cytokines: At the interface of immunology and endocrinology. *Cellular Immunology*, 252(1), 91–110. doi: 10.1016/j.cellimm.2007.09.010.

[18] Pavlov, V. A. & Tracey, K. J. (2012). The vagus nerve & the inflammatory reflex—linking immunity & metabolism. *Nature Reviews Endocrinology*, 8(12), 743. doi: 10.1038/nrendo.2012.189.

[19] Saturn, S. R. (2017). Two factors that fuel compassion: The oxytocin system and the social experience of moral elevation. *Oxford handbook of compassion science*, 121-132. doi: 10.1093/oxfordhb/9780190464684.013.10.

[20] Gamer, M., Zurowski, B. & Büchel, C. (2010). Different amygdala subregions mediate valence-related and

attentional effects of oxytocin in humans. *Proceedings of the National Academy of Sciences*, 107(20), 9400-9405. doi: 10.1073/pnas.1000985107.

[21] Kirsch, P., Esslinger, C., Gallhofer, B. & Meyer-Lindenberg, A. (2005). Oxytocin modulates neural circuitry for social cognition and fear in humans. *The Journal of Neuroscience: The Official Journal of the Society for Neuroscience*, 25(49), 11489–11493. doi: 10.1523/JNEUROSCI.3984-05.2005.

[22] Holt-Lunstad, J., Birmingham, W. A. & Light, K. C. (2008). Influence of a 'warm touch' support enhancement intervention among married couples on ambulatory blood pressure, oxytocin, alpha amylase, and cortisol. *Psychosomatic Medicine*, 70(9), 976–985. doi: 10.1097/PSY.0b013e318187aef7.

[23] Wang, P., Yang, H. P., Tian, S., Wang, L., Wang, S. C., Zhang, F. & Wang, Y. F. (2015). Oxytocin-secreting system: A major part of the neuroendocrine center regulating immunologic activity. *Journal of Neuroimmunology*, 289, 152–161. doi: 10.1016/j.jneuroim.2015.11.001.

[24] Gutkowska, J. & Jankowski, M. (2012). Oxytocin revisited: its role in cardiovascular regulation. *Journal of Neuroendocrinology*, 24(4), 599–608. doi: 10.1111/j.1365-2826.2011.02235.x.

[25] Szeto, A., Nation, D. A., & McCabe, P. M. (2008). Oxytocin attenuates NADPH-dependent superoxide activity and IL-6 secretion in macrophages and vascular cells. American *Journal of Physiology-Endocrinology and Metabolism*, 295(6), E1495-E1501. doi: 10.1152/ajpendo.90718.2008.

[26] Bhat, A. H., Dar, K. B., Anees, S., Zargar, M. A., Masood, A., Sofi, M. A. & Ganie, S. A. (2015). Oxidative stress, mitochondrial dysfunction and neurodegenerative diseases; a mechanistic insight. *Biomedicine & Pharmacotherapy*, 74, 101–110. doi: 10.1016/j.biopha.2015.07.025.

Chapter 5
Self-Kindness

Self-kindness is a kick-ass life skill. - Tamara Yeow London School of Economics master's student

What is the greatest challenge you face right now? In life we face two types of challenges. Those we willingly seek out, such as applying for a new job, and those that life thrusts upon us, such as ill health or the many difficulties caused by COVID-19. How we overcome both types of challenge is perhaps one measure of how well we are doing in life and self-kindness empowers us to succeed in doing so.

You might be sceptical of self-kindness. It sounds self-indulgent. But this is a misunderstanding. Self-kindness is not about going soft on yourself. It is not about pandering to your every whim or staying in bed all day. It is not about lowering your ambitions, standards, or expectations of yourself. In fact, at times, self-kindness may require us to work more and be fierce and tough in order to self-protect.

So, what exactly is self-kindness? Self-kindness is treating yourself as you would a loved family member or a best friend[1]. When your best friend needs you, you listen to them, you support them and you value them unconditionally. Understood and applied correctly, self-kindness supports optimum physical and mental health, helps you to perform at your peak in high-stakes situations, enhances the quality of your relationships and, above all, helps you take on the challenges you must surmount if you are to grow and become the best that you can be.

These are not empty claims. Ever since psychologists Kirstin Neff[1] and Chris Germer[2] started to research self-kindness and its namesake, self-compassion, 20 years ago, there has been a growing body of research evidencing the benefits of this approach. These range from improving academic performance in university students, to quicker recovery from injury for athletes, to reducing post-traumatic stress in war veterans[3&4]. As a result, elite universities, such as Stanford and Cambridge, deliver self-kindness workshops to students, the Harvard Business Review[5] has published articles endorsing the benefits of self-kindness, and occupational psychologists run self-kindness training in workplaces[6].

Self-kindness works because it gives us two powerful resources: enhanced emotional self-regulation and psychological safety. Enhanced emotional regulation means that in challenging situations, we are better able to reduce the impact of distressing emotions on our ability to perform. This makes self-kindness particularly valuable when facing the unsolicited challenges life throws at us. When faced with such challenges, our emotional threat system is activated, causing us stress, anxiety and fear. Whilst initially some fear, anxiety and stress can be useful, too much has a detrimental effect on our intellectual and physical performance, as illustrated by the bell-shaped curve in the graph below[7&8].

Fig. 5. Bell-shaped curve showing relationship between performance and stress [7&8]

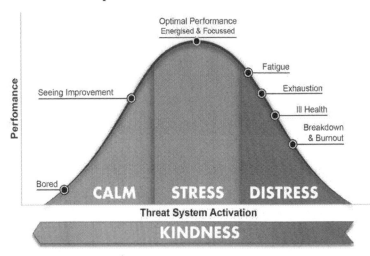

Self-kindness helps by reducing activation of the emotional threat system and boosting activation of our soothing system, calming us down and therefore minimising the negative effects of excessive stress and anxiety on our thinking, behaviour and overall performance[9&10]. This enables to you to handle the difficult meeting with the boss, the serious illness of a family member, or whatever life challenges you face, with greater clarity, poise, wisdom, compassion and confidence.

For many, personal relationships can sometimes be a source of challenge. Self-kindness enables us to be less emotionally needy, more supportive of others, and reduces the distress caused by any altercations and conflicts we do have. This makes us less likely to dwell on feelings of anger or resentment which can lead to behaviours that undermine our relationships. Self-kindness also helps to avoid or diffuse tension in the first place. Therefore, self-kindness is good for our friendships, our family lives and our love lives too[11].

When it comes to the challenges we actively seek out in order to grow, such as applying for new jobs, self-kindness helps us again, by fostering psychological safety. You have the potential to achieve amazing things, but having potential is not the same as the same as realising it. Crossing the gap between having the potential for success and transforming that potential into the actual reality of success can be hard.

The obstacles to fulfilling our potential are either external obstacles such as insufficient time or money, or internal psycho-emotional obstacles such as insufficient confidence and fear of failure. Whatever their cause, self-kindness makes overcoming such obstacles and realising our potential easier. Self-kindness entails valuing yourself unconditionally, which means your self-esteem is not dependent on accomplishments and successes. As a result, failure does not hurt or scare so much. This is a big advantage.

Before learning about self-kindness I, like many people, derived self-esteem from successes and positive comparisons with others. Psychologists call this "contingent self-esteem"[12]. You feel great when things go well, but failure becomes an attack on one's self-esteem and it hurts. The mind instinctively seeks to protect you from more of such pain. You therefore experience considerable fear of failure, resist doing the things that might result in failure, and can succumb to procrastination and excuse-making, both tricks of the mind intended to protect you from pain. This makes it harder, or downright impossible, to convert your potential to do great things, into the reality of doing them.

By committing to self-kindness and valuing yourself unconditionally, you short-circuit the *failure, drop in self-esteem, pain* pathway. Of course, you will still be disappointed when things go wrong, but your mind will not interpret failure as an assault on self-esteem. In this way, self-kindness makes it safer for you to take on the really big challenges that you must take on if you are to realise the full extent of your potential. Such challenges inevitably come with a risk of failure, but self-kindness emboldens you to embrace them fully.

A second benefit of the psychological safety self-kindness gives us is we feel less compelled to conform and to do things out of a need for validation. Liberated from these constraints it becomes easier to discover and accept our individual and unique pattern of strengths, talents and weaknesses. It is then easier to create a life, a career and ways of contributing to the world that allow us to develop the full breadth of our strengths and talents. Self-kindness helps you to be more *you* in the world! It helps us to to be the best that we can be and lead a truly fulfilling life.

To apply self-kindness, think of how you treat a best friend, particularly when they having a tough time. You listen, support and value them. Similarly, self-kindness requires you to listen to yourself, in the sense of noticing your thoughts, feelings and physical sensations. By listening to and tuning into yourself, in the present moment, with acceptance and without judgement (referred to as mindfulness), you reduce the likelihood of getting caught up in negative thought cycles which exacerbate distress[13].

Supporting ourselves can be done by using encouraging and supportive self-talk. The emotional centres in the brain are highly sensitive to tone of voice,[14&15] so it is important to use a soft inner voice tone rather than a neutral or even harsh voice tone, which actually many of us tend to use when talking and thinking to ourselves. In addition to talking to ourselves silently in our minds, we can externalise it, by writing a self-kindness text message, email or letter from the perspective of a kind friend. These techniques may seem silly, but for Mariama, the client of mine who sent herself a supportive text message prior to a job interview, it soothed her nerves, and she got the job. Similarly, for David, the client who wrote a long letter to himself after a relationship breakup, it helped greatly too. Supporting ourselves can also involve concrete actions, such as giving ourselves reasonable breaks during a long workday, making time to exercise and making an effort to eat and sleep well.

Finally, self-kindness involves remembering to value ourselves unconditionally. This means we do not let our sense of self-worth be entirely determined by outcomes or other people's evaluations of us. This makes failure and the threat of negative evaluation far less threatening which, paradoxically, make us more able to achieve and succeed.

By adopting self-kindness we not only help ourselves, but in a small way we may help change the world. Self-kindness makes it easier to acknowledge and accept our vulnerabilities, the fragility of our human lives and the inevitable suffering in life. This also makes it easier to see vulnerability in others and understand that our vulnerability is shared and a defining feature of our common humanity. At an individual level, connecting with others through a sense of shared vulnerability facilitates high-quality relationships. At a collective level, if we can scale our ability to connect through a sense of shared vulnerability to all in society and across the world, regardless of differences, we create the conditions where kindness and compassion become a more dominant motive in how our global society operates.

References

[1] Neff, K. (2011) *Self-compassion*, New York: HarperCollins.

[2] Germer, C. (2009) *The Mindfulness Path to Self-compassion*, New York: Guildford Press.

[3] Dahm, K. A., Meyer, E. C., Neff, K. D., Kimbrel, N. A., Gulliver, S. B., & Morissette, S. B. (2015). Mindfulness, self-compassion, posttraumatic stress disorder symptoms, and functional disability in US Iraq and Afghanistan war

veterans. *Journal of Traumatic Stress*, *28*(5), 460-464. doi: 10.1002/jts.22045.

[4] Barnard, L. K., & Curry, J. F. (2011). Self-compassion: Conceptualizations, correlates, & interventions. *Review of general psychology*, *15*(4), 289-303. doi: 10.1037/a0025754.

[5] Germer. C (2017) To Recover from Failure, Try Some Self-Compassion: *Harvard Business Review*, January 5th 2017 https://hbr.org/2017/01/to-recover-from-failure-try-some-self-compassion [accessed 12-06-21].

[6] Super, A., (2019) *Exploring the Development of Self-Compassion in the Workplace*. Professional Doctorate in Occupational and Business Psychology Thesis, Kingston University.

[7] Salehi, B., Cordero, M. I., & Sandi, C. (2010). Learning under stress: the inverted-U-shape function revisited. *Learning & memory*, *17*(10), 522-530. doi: 10.1101/lm.1914110.

[8] Sapolsky, R. M. (2015). Stress and the brain: individual variability and the inverted-U. *Nature neuroscience*, *18*(10), 1344. doi: 10.1038/nn.4109.

[9] Allen, A. B., & Leary, M. R. (2010). Self-Compassion, stress, and coping. *Social and personality psychology compass*, *4*(2), 107-118. doi: 10.1111/j.1751-9004.2009.00246.

[10] Barczak, N., & Eklund, R. C. (2020). The moderating effect of self-compassion on relationships between performance and subsequent coping and motivation. *International Journal of Sport and Exercise Psychology*, *18*(2), 256-268. doi: 10.1080/1612197X.2018.1511620.

[11] Jacobson, E. H. K., Wilson, K. G., Kurz, A. S., & Kellum, K. K. (2018). Examining self-compassion in romantic relationships. *Journal of Contextual Behavioral Science*, *8*, 69-73.

[12] Kernis, M. H., & Goldman, B. M. (2006). Assessing stability of self-esteem and contingent self-esteem. *Self-esteem issues and answers: A sourcebook of current perspectives*, 77-85.

[13] Verplanken, B., & Fisher, N. (2014). Habitual worrying and benefits of mindfulness. *Mindfulness*, *5*(5), 566-573. doi: 10.1007/s12671-013-0211-0.

[14] Sauter, D. A., Eisner, F., Calder, A. J., & Scott, S. K. (2010). Perceptual cues in nonverbal vocal expressions of emotion. *Quarterly Journal of Experimental Psychology*, *63*(11), 2251-2272. doi: 10.1080/17470211003721642.

[15] Ethofer, T., Van De Ville, D., Scherer, K., & Vuilleumier, P. (2009). Decoding of emotional information in voice-sensitive cortices. *Current biology*, *19*(12), 1028-1033. doi: 10.1016/j.cub.2009.04.054.

Chapter 6

Kindness to Those Closest to Us: Partners, Family and Friends

To the world you may be one person, but to one person you may be the world. - Dr. Seuss

Kindness in words creates confidence. Kindness in thinking creates profoundness. Kindness in giving creates love. - Lao Tzu

Being kind to those closest to us ought to be easy since in theory we love and care for them, but we all know that at times it can be hard. Sometimes, it is hard to know what the kind thing to do is. For example, parents generally want to be kind to their children, but is it kinder to adopt an understanding approach and soft form of discipline with a misbehaving child, or actually, in the long run, is it kinder to use a harsher form of discipline? Such quandaries underscore the need for applying intelligent kindness, which means kindness informed by scientific research into what really does lead to optimal outcomes. High-quality, evidence-based parenting guidance is increasingly available, for example, on the websites of the American Psychological Association[1] or the Family Lives[2] organisation in the UK.

In other circumstances, there is no confusion as to what the kindest course of action towards another person is, but we can feel that being kind is an obligation inherent to the relationship. Being kind then becomes a matter of duty and an expectation which, at times, can generate frustration and even resentment, especially if we perceive that our actions are not sufficiently appreciated. That said, there are many ways in which people in close relationships have the possibility of acting freely and being kind to each other. Indeed, kindness and reciprocal care provide the foundation for lasting friendships and partnerships and are critical for the health and growth of bonds between people.

The quality of our close personal relationships is one of the greatest determining factors of an individual's wellbeing[3]. Therefore, investing in relationships and growing our capacity for kindness ought to be a priority. Additionally, bringing up children in an environment infused with kindness will develop their own ability to be kind and have nurturing relationships with others[4]. It will also develop their capacity for self-kindness, strengthening their resilience and ability to succeed under pressure[4].

Of course, to a large extent, we all know the importance of kindness, but at times being kind is hard and our human nature is complex. Just as people can be kind, they can be nasty too. Emotional and physical abuse of partners and the elderly is a significant and insufficiently addressed problem across the world. In the UK, domestic abuse will affect one in four women and one in six men, and leads to two women being murdered every week, and 30 men being murdered a year[5].

The statistics on child abuse and bullying are just as shocking, with the National Society for the Prevention of Cruelty to Children reporting that 50,000 children in the U.K. have been identified as needing protection from abuse[6], and the UK Department for Education reporting that 40 per cent of 14-15 year-olds were bullied in 2018[7]. The United Nations predicted a 20 per cent rise in domestic abuse as a result/ of the COVID-19 lockdown. This is equivalent to 15 million more cases as a result of a three-month lockdown in which victims were confined with an abuser[8&9]. Such data illustrates the tremendously tricky nature of the human mind. It is a mind that enables horrible nastiness to be committed to individuals towards whom one is supposed to be in a nurturing relationship. Arguably many of us are capable of committing abuse.

One way to make partial sense of what occurs in the mind of those who commit abuse is that in their relationship to their own selves there is a lack of self-acceptance and self-love, and therefore a sense of inadequacy, leading to feelings of hurt, fear, shame and anger[10,11,12&13]. This leads to heightened activation of, and the dominance of, their emotional threat system[14]. Lack of insight and ability to regulate their emotions means that their mind seeks to avoid control and counteract the painful emotions, by a mixture of exerting pain onto others and controlling them. These are effectively the core ingredients of abuse[15]. In this way, the actions of someone who perpetuates abuse can be interpreted as an awfully dysfunctional response to their internal psychological pain, as encapsulated in the adage, 'hurt people, hurt people'.

A commitment to kindness is an important part of the solution. A commitment to kindness, as individuals, families and communities, would require us to do much more to take bold courageous action to prevent and stop abuse. An increase in kindness, in society, communities, families and interpersonal relationships, could promote conditions in which it becomes easier for abusers and potential abusers to allow themselves to feel sufficiently vulnerable to acknowledge, articulate, face and start to work through their own pain and fears. This could help reduce or eliminate the emotional and psychological drivers of the perverse behaviour.

More self-kindness could help abusers heal their hurts and wounds[16] and give victims the strength to remove themselves from abusive situations and work towards recovering from their trauma[17]. It is important to underscore that real kindness can require considerable strength, bravery and toughness; for example, when facing up to an abuser[18]. At times, kindness needs to be fierce.

Achieving greater kindness in our communities, families and interpersonal relationships is down to all of us. We are all networked into a series of relationships. We all have a circle of influence and people upon whose lives we can have an impact. By cultivating our capacity for kindness, we inject more kindness into our network of relationships, bringing the benefits of kindness to others, and our own selves.

To cultivate kindness we start simply by making a commitment to being kind more often and in new ways. Most of us know how to be kind, but we can also make use of the guidance and science-based training programmes that have been developed to specifically train our minds to strengthen the neural networks that underpin our capacity for kindness[19,20&21]. The links section of the 'Resources' page on the Kindness Advantage website provides a list of training programmes informed by scientific research designed to cultivate kindness and compassion[22]. Training our capacity for kindness is like developing any other skill: with regular practice we get better. We can start by making an effort to better notice distress, or opportunities to promote wellbeing in others and follow up with kind action. We can also seek to observe what makes it easier for us to be kind, and what makes it harder for us to be kind. By identifying our personal facilitators and inhibitors of kindness we can then identify what we can do to promote the facilitators and reduce the inhibitors. We can also use creativity and imagination to discover new ways of being kind and encouraging kindness. Within families and among couples, kindness can manifest through speech, acts of service, spending quality time, giving gifts or donating resources and where appropriate, reassuring or affectionate touch[23]. Parents, particularly those with young children, can explicitly and implicitly teach ways of being kind to others as well as the self, by practising random acts of kindness, or by keeping a kindness journal or kindness wall chart on which kind acts given and received are recorded. Young people experiencing and expressing kindness is especially important, not only for protecting and boosting mental health, but also for supporting effective learning and memory, as discussed in the next chapter.

Kindness will be expressed differently in different contexts. How kindness manifests between a parent and child at home will differ to how it is expressed at work between a manager and employee. But kindness is always important. In fact, our ability to be kind at home is significantly influenced by what happens during the working day[24]. If you have experienced a distinct lack of kindness at work, it makes it more difficult to be kind at home. Kindness at work, therefore, not only has beneficial impacts on work performance, as explained in Chapter Eight, it also supports people's capacity for kindness in their personal lives. This underscores the need for managers and organisational leader to prioritise kindness for themselves and their employees[24].

Being kind to those close to us can be challenging, but boosting the amount of kindness in our relationships with family and friends brings innumerable benefits. As a society we now have available scientifically-backed methods for training kindness which we can scale. It simply requires us, you and me, to commit to and work on developing our capacity for kindness.

References

[1] American Psychological Association (2020) *Psychology Topics, Parenting.* https://www.apa.org/topics/parenting/ [Accessed 04-06-21].

[2] Family Lives (2020) https://www.familylives.org.uk/ [Accessed 17-06-21].

[3] Dush, C. M. K., & Amato, P. R. (2005). Consequences of relationship status and quality for subjective well-being. *Journal of Social and Personal Relationships*, *22*(5), 607-62. doi: 10.1177/0265407505056438.

[4] Greenland, S. K. (2010). *The mindful child: How to help your kid manage stress and become happier, kinder, and more compassionate.* New York: Simon and Schuster.

[5] LWA (2020) Livingwithoutabuse *Statistics* https://www.lwa.org.uk/understanding-abuse/statistics.htm [Accessed 17-06-21].

[6] National Society for the Protection of Cruelty Against Children (2020) https://www.nspcc.org.uk/about-us/performance-plans-strategy/ [Accessed 17-06-21].

[7] HMSO, (2020)UK Department for Education. *Bullying in England.* https://assets.publishing.service.gov.uk/government/uploads/system/uploads/attachment_data/file/754959/Bullying_in _England_2013-2018.pdf [Accessed 17-06-21].

[8] Rosenthal, C. M., & Thompson, L. A. (2020). Child Abuse Awareness Month during the coronavirus disease 2019 pandemic. *JAMA pediatrics*. 174(8):812. doi: 10.1001/jamapediatrics.2020.1459.

[9] United Nations Population Fund (2020) "Impact of the COVID-19 Pandemic on Family Planning and Ending Gender-based Violence, Female Genital Mutilation and Child Marriage"

Available at https://www.unfpa.org/resources/impact-covid-19-pandemic-family-planning-and-ending-gender-based-violence-female-genital [Accessed 04-06-21].

[10] Dorahy, M. J., & Clearwater, K. (2012). Shame and guilt in men exposed to childhood sexual abuse: A qualitative investigation. *Journal of child sexual abuse*, *21*(2), 155-175. doi: 10.1080/10538712.2012.659803.

[11] Hershkowitz, I., Lanes, O., & Lamb, M. E. (2007). Exploring the disclosure of child sexual abuse with alleged victims and their parents. *Child abuse & neglect*, *31*(2), 111-123. doi: 10.1016/j.chiabu.2006.09.004.

[12] Sorsoli, L. (2004). Hurt feelings: Emotional abuse and the failure of empathy. *Journal of emotional abuse*, *4*(1), 1-26. doi: 10.1300/J135v04n01_01.

[13] Zweig, J. M., Lachman, P., Yahner, J., & Dank, M. (2014). Correlates of cyber dating abuse among teens. *Journal of Youth and Adolescence*, *43*(8), 1306-1321. doi: 10.1007/s10964-013-0047-x.

[14] Spielberg, J. M., Olino, T. M., Forbes, E. E., & Dahl, R. E. (2014). Exciting fear in adolescence: Does pubertal development alter threat processing?. *Developmental cognitive neuroscience*, *8*, 86-95. doi: 10.1016/j.dcn.2014.01.004.

[15] Romero-Martínez, A., Figueiredo, B., & Moya-Albiol, L. (2014). Childhood history of abuse and child abuse potential: The role of parent's gender and timing of childhood abuse. *Child abuse & neglect*, *38*(3), 510-516. doi: 10.1016/j.chiabu.2013.09.010.

[16] Neff, K. D. (2016). The self-compassion scale is a valid and theoretically coherent measure of self-compassion. *Mindfulness*, *7*(1), 264-274. doi: https://doi.org/10.1007/s12671-016-0560-6.

[17] Vettese, L. C., Dyer, C. E., Li, W. L., & Wekerle, C. (2011). Does self-compassion mitigate the association between

childhood maltreatment and later emotion regulation difficulties? A preliminary investigation. *International Journal of Mental Health and Addiction*, *9*(5), 480. doi: 10.1007/s11469-011-9340-7.

[18] Bruton, C. (2015). Stories of strength, survival and the system. *DVRCV Advocate*, (2), 25.

[19] CMT, (2020) Compassionate Mind Foundation. *Resources* https://www.compassionatemind.co.uk/resources https://compassionatemind.co.uk/ [accessed 16-06-21].

[20] CBCT (2020) Emory University's Cognitively-Based Compassion Training at https://www.compassion.emory.edu/cbct-compassion-training/index.html [Accessed 17-06-21].

[21] CCT (2020) Stanford University's Compassion Cultivation Training http://ccare.stanford.edu/education/about-compassion-cultivation-training-cct/ [Accessed 17-06-21].

[22] Kindness Advantage (2020) *Kindness Advantages Resources & Links* https://kindness-advantage.com/links [accessed 16-06-21].

[23] Chapman, G.D., 2015. *The five love languages: The secret to love that lasts*. New York: Northfield Publishing.

[24] Lourel, M., Ford, M.T., Gamassou, C.E., Guéguen, N. and Hartmann, A., 2009. Negative and positive spillover between work and home. *Journal of Managerial Psychology*. 24 (1). doi: 10.1108/02683940910959762.

Chapter 7

Kindness for Learning and Education

The mission of schools must include teaching kindness. Without it, communities, families, schools, and classrooms become places of incivility where lasting learning is unlikely to take place... Kindness can be taught... It belongs in every home, school, neighborhood, and society. - Professor Maurice Elias

Learning involves understanding new things, acquiring new knowledge and skills, remembering them and being able to apply them in novel situations and contexts. Teaching is the facilitation of this process and education is the systematic way in which teaching and learning are organised.

The ability to learn quickly is ever more essential in a world in which the pace of change is increasingly rapid. Enhanced learning ability is a differential advantage, not only for individuals but organisations and businesses too. So, knowing how to improve learning is important for success.

Identifying ways to improve learning is especially relevant to schools, colleges and universities, of course. Unfortunately, educational outcomes vary greatly with many young people failing to fulfil their potential. Education systems in developed nations face considerable challenges in the form of increasing attainment gaps between students of different socio-economic status and ethnicity[1], increased violence in schools[2&3], increased mental illness among students[4,5&6] and increased burnout and rates of attrition among teachers[7&8].

Prioritising kindness has to be part of the solution to the challenge of improving learning and educational outcomes. Both neuroscience and classroom-based research evidence the advantages of kindness for learning and education. Two neuroscience research findings in particular are relevant. Firstly, the brain is a social organ and its ability to perceive, interpret, encode and retrieve information is optimised when these processes occur in the context of rewarding relationships[9]. Secondly, emotional distress places a significant burden on working memory and attentional control[10], both of which are related to functioning of the prefrontal cortex region of the brain[11] (see Fig. 6). These cognitive resources are essential for learning[12]. Therefore, the emotional context in which learning occurs is more important than was previously realised, as distressing emotions are highly damaging to learning[9].

Kindness, therefore, boosts learning. Firstly, kindness supports meaningful, positive and rewarding connections between people, and when this occurs in a learning situation, the processing of new information becomes more socially relevant. As a consequence, the brain encodes the new information more effectively, making it more memorable and enhancing the quality of the learning process. Secondly, in environments where kindness predominates, learners experience less distressing emotions. Distressing emotions usurp cognitive resources[10]. Therefore, diminishing or removing distressing emotions frees up cognitive resources for learning. One way in which this occurs is through the action of the neuropeptide oxytocin, released from the brain's pituitary gland (see Fig. 6 below) when we experience kindness or trust with another person[13] as discussed in Chapter Four. Oxytocin has been shown to reduce the responsiveness of the brain's neural circuitry responsible for threat and fear, specifically the

Fig. 6. The prefrontal cortex (PFC), pituitary gland and amygdala (sagittal plane).

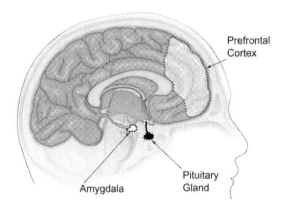

amygdalae[14], thus making us more resilient and less susceptible to the cognitive performance-limiting effects of anxiety. The advantages of kindness are backed up by data obtained through research in primary and secondary schools[15&16] and universities[17&18]. For example, a randomised control trial of an intervention which encouraged kindness among primary school children found that grades and social competence skills improved[16].

In universities, kindness also enhances outcomes. Currently 50 universities across the world have incorporated into their curricula a compassion training programme developed at the University of Hertfordshire[19] in the UK. When university students are partly assessed on their ability to interact with kindness during seminar discussions, grades and wellbeing improve[17&19]. Students are taught to demonstrate kindness in seminars by, for instance, encouraging less confident students to contribute to the discussion, using respectful open body language and eye contact and using supportive, inclusive and non-discriminatory language. When kindness among students is prioritised in this way, research also shows the frequency of intellectual insights and the level of co-operation in group work increases significantly[17&19]. Furthermore, when previously there was a considerable academic attainment gap between black and ethnic minority students compared to white students, following introduction of kindness into the curriculum, this gap ceases to exist.

Teaching students self-kindness, often described as self-compassion, by for instance treating themselves in times of difficulty as they would treat a best friend and using encouraging and supportive self-talk, has also been shown to be highly beneficial. Studies demonstrate that teaching self-compassion improves students' motivation[20], wellbeing[21&22] and resilience[23], as well as reducing procrastination[24]: all factors that support learning and performance in examinations[25].

Finally, research with employees at Google, as to what enabled some of their teams to learn and perform better than others, revealed that their highest-performing teams excelled at making all members feel safe[26]. These teams achieved this by treating each other with care and respect, particularly with regard to how they spoke to each other in meetings. The team members were also skilled at understanding how others felt, on the basis of nonverbal cues, and behaving appropriately. These kindness-based behaviours were responsible for raising the collective intelligence of the team.

In summary, kindness supports the brain's ability to learn, be emotionally resilient and feel good. Kindness can be taught and promoted at all levels of education and doing so improves academic, as well as emotional and social, development. When kindness is prioritised in organisations, performance, learning and collective intelligence also improve. If we want to enhance learning and educational outcomes, focusing on promoting kindness is one of the most important things we must do.

References

[1] Mowat, J. G. (2018). Closing the attainment gap – a realistic proposition or an elusive pipe-dream?. *Journal of Education Policy*, *33*(2), 299-321. doi: 10.1080/02680939.2017.1352033.

[2] Böckler, N., Seeger, T., Sitzer, P., and Heitmeyer, W. (2013). "School Shootings: Conceptual Framework and International Empirical Trends". *In School Shootings: International Research, Case Studies, and Concepts for Prevention*, edited by N. Böckler *et al.*New York: Springer. doi: 10.1007/978-1-4614-5526-4.

[3] Ponsford, R., Thompson, C. and Paparini, S., (2019). We need a renewed focus on primary prevention to tackle youth knife violence. *BMJ*, *365*, p.l1769. doi: 10.1136/bmj.l1769.

[4] Geulayov, G., Kapur, N., Turnbull, P., Clements, C., Waters, K., Ness, J., ... & Hawton, K. (2016). Epidemiology and trends in non-fatal self-harm in three centres in England, 2000–2012: findings from the Multicentre Study of Self-harm in England. *BMJ open*, *6*(4), e010538. doi: 10.1136/bmjopen-2015-010538.

[5] Keski-Rahkonen, A., & Mustelin, L. (2016). Epidemiology of eating disorders in Europe: prevalence, incidence, comorbidity, course, consequences, and risk factors. *Current opinion in psychiatry*, *29*(6), 340-345. doi: 10.1097/YCO.0000000000000278.

[6] Shain, B., (2016). Suicide and suicide attempts in adolescents. *Pediatrics*, *138*(1), p.e20161420. doi: 10.1542/peds.2016-1420.

[7] Arnup, J., & Bowles, T. (2016). Should I stay or should I go? Resilience as a protective factor for teachers' intention to leave the teaching profession. *Australian Journal of Education*, *60*(3), 229-244. doi: 10.1177/0004944116667620.

[8] Lindqvist, P. and Nordänger, UK, (2016). Already elsewhere–A study of (skilled) teachers' choice to leave teaching. *Teaching and Teacher Education*, *54*, pp.88-97. doi: 10.1016/j.tate.2015.11.010.

[9] Cozolino, L., (2013). *The Social Neuroscience of Education: Optimizing Attachment and Learning in the Classroom The Norton Series on the Social Neuroscience of Education)*. WW Norton & Company.

[10] Eysenck & Derakshan (2011). New perspectives in attentional control theory. *Personality and Individual Differences*, *50*(7), pp.955-960. doi: 10.1016/j.paid.2010.08.019.

[11] Curtis, C. E., & D'Esposito, M. (2003). Persistent activity in the prefrontal cortex during working memory. *Trends in cognitive sciences*, 7(9), 415-423. doi: 10.1016/S1364-6613(03)00197-9.

[12] Meltzer, L. (Ed.). (2018). *Executive function in education: From theory to practice*. New York: Guilford Publications.

[13] Saturn, S. R. (2017). *Two Factors That Fuel Compassion*: In: The Oxford Handbook of Compassion Science. Seppälä, (E. M et al., (Eds) Vol. 1). Oxford University Press. doi: 10.1093/oxfordhb/9780190464684.013.10.

[14] Insel, T.R., (2010). The challenge of translation in social neuroscience: a review of oxytocin, vasopressin, and affiliative behavior. *Neuron*, *65*(6), pp.768-779. doi: 10.1016/j.neuron.2010.03.005.

[15] Binfet, J.T. and Passmore, H.A., (2017). Teachers' Perceptions of Kindness at School. *International Journal of Emotional Education*, 9(1), pp.37-53.

[16] Flook, L., Goldberg, S.B., Pinger, L. and Davidson, R.J., (2015). Promoting prosocial behavior and self-regulatory skills in preschool children through a mindfulness-based kindness curriculum. *Developmental psychology*, *51*(1), p.44. doi: 10.1037/a0038256.

[17] Gilbert, T., (2016), June. Embedding and assessing compassion in the university curriculum. In *The International Academic Forum*. *The International Academic Forum*. Available at https://uhra.herts.ac.uk/handle/2299/17435 [Accessed 28-05-21].

[18] Zajonc, A., (2013). Contemplative pedagogy: A quiet revolution in higher education. *New Directions for Teaching and Learning*, 134, pp.83-94.

[19] Gilbert, T., Doolan, NTF, M., Beka, S., Spencer, N., Crotta, M. and Davari, S., (2018). Compassion on university degree programmes at a UK university: The neuroscience of effective group work. Available at *Journal of Research in Innovative Teaching & Learning*, *11*(1), pp.4-21.

[20] Wagner, L. K., Schindler, S., & Reinhard, M. A. (2017). The Positive Facet of Self-compassion Predicts Self-reported Use of and Attitudes toward Desirable Difficulties in Learning. *Frontiers.* doi: 10.3389/fpsyg.2017.01353.

[21] Neff, K. D. & McGeehee, P. (2010). Self-compassion and psychological resilience among adolescents and young adults. *Self and Identity*, 9, 225-240. doi: 10.1080/15298860902979307.

[22] Neff, K. D., & Costigan, A. P. (2014). Self-compassion, wellbeing, and happiness. *Psychologie in Österreich*, 114-117.

[23] Zhang, Y., Luo, X., Che, X., & Duan, W. (2016). Protective Effect of Self-Compassion to Emotional Response among Students with Chronic Academic Stress. *Frontiers in Psychology*, *7*. doi: 10.3389/fpsyg.2016.01802.

[24] Sirois, F. M. (2014). Procrastination and stress: Exploring the role of self-compassion. *Self And Identity*, *13*(2), 128-145. doi: 10.1080/15298868.2013.763404.

[25] Richardson, M., Abraham, C. and Bond, R., (2012). Psychological correlates of university students' academic performance: A systematic review and meta-analysis. *Psychological bulletin*, *138*(2), p.353. doi: 10.1037/a0026838.

[26] Duhigg, C. (2016). What Google learned from its quest to build the perfect team. *New York Times Magazine*. 25th February. Available at: http://www.nytimes.com/2016/02/28/magazine/what-google-learned- from-its-quest-to-build-the-perfect-team. [Accessed 20-05-21].

Chapter 8

Kindness for the Workplace and Organisational Success

Managing compassionately is not just a better way to build a team, it's a better way to build a company. - Jeff Weiner, LinkedIn CEO

Kindness at work may seem like an oxymoron. Indeed, the majority of employees don't particularly enjoy work, nor feel that they experience much kindness in the workplace. According to a global survey, 87 per cent of the employed workforce worldwide is unmotivated and uncommitted to their work[1]. Stress and anxiety caused by work-related issues is now recognised as a significant problem in terms of lost productivity. Arguably, more importantly, stress and anxiety caused by work-related issues are also the most common factor triggering suicides in men. The fact that there are 20 per cent more heart attacks on Mondays[2] is likely related to the negative emotions that going back to work elicits in many employees.

Organisations large and small, both publicly and privately funded, play a significant role in all of our lives. We all rely upon organisations to make our lives happen and many of us will spend the 100,000 hours of the average work life in an organisation[3].

It is therefore in everybody's interest that organisations perform well and that those of us who are employees of organisations do not experience stress, fear or become ill because of work. Instead, workers should feel supported, respected and able to thrive. For this, we need organisations "to be truly human", to quote the late Pierre Nanterm, visionary former CEO of multinational professional services company, Accenture[4].

Kindness is the key that enables organisations to be more human, reduce suffering, promote wellbeing[5] and unlock extraordinary individual, team and organisational performance[6.] Big claims, yes, but if we stop to think about it, it makes sense and there is mounting research indicating that kindness in an organisation is a key driver of differential, and competitive, advantage.

When people operate in a kind environment, they feel safe from social threats, which in turn means they can devote all their energy and attention to their work. It also makes it safer to be creative, to give feedback and speak honestly. This enables rapid learning from mistakes, supports innovation, safety and optimal team performance as evidenced by Harvard professor, Amy Edmondson's, research[7]. When information flows more freely and quickly within a team or organisation, problems are averted and creative solutions found more readily. In industries in which speedy, co-ordinated teamwork is required, such as in healthcare, emergency services, travel services and the hospitality sector, kindness is essential for ensuring that levels of trust, information flow and collaborative problem-solving are optimised.

Research has shown that the fundamental element behind the success of Southwest Airlines, the world's leading airline for total number of passengers flown annually[8], is their culture of care, support, egalitarianism and kindness among all employees[9]. To maintain profitability, operational efficiency is paramount. This requires cooperation between different people with different roles and levels of status. These differences can thwart rapid, good quality communication and co-operation. However, kindness dissolves people problems and facilitates seamless co-operation and communication[10]. Similar findings from healthcare research show that kindness and compassion among healthcare professionals and allied staff fuels the optimised collaborative and coordinated work that ensures excellent patient care[11].

Research also demonstrates that enabling employees to be kind, both to each other and customers, is strongly associated with engagement at work[6], motivation[12] and wellbeing[13]. Acting with kindness can give workers a greater sense of meaning and purpose. In this way, kindness in the workplace also has positive implications for recruitment and talent retention. A study examined performance across forty different business teams in a Fortune 500 retail company. When employees of a business team rated kindness as a value shown by their team, they had better financial performance and achieved higher customer retention. The authors of the study concluded that business leaders and managers need to recognise that there are organisational and individual benefits to be gained by making it easier for employees to be kind[14]. What is more, kindness improves an organisation's ability to adapt to change, making it more agile and resilient. Studies have shown that the extent to which employees felt their managers were supportive of them in their approach to downsizing and laying people off was related to productivity and customer retention[15].

Some sources of suffering are an inevitable part of life. In any organisation there will be people suffering from the trials and tribulations of life. Other sources of suffering can originate from organisations themselves, especially if, for example, people feel undermined, disrespected, expected to achieve unreasonable targets or constantly under threat.

Organisations can demonstrate they care for their people by considering at a system level how to respond with kindness to the inevitable suffering in the lives of their employees, as well as how to promote wellbeing and avoid causing distress through their own actions. To do this, organisations need to prioritise the value of kindness. One way to do this is to identify and remove inhibitors of kindness and identify and promote facilitators of kindness within an organisation's procedures, culture and its leaders.

When people operate in an environment in which they feel cared for and have opportunities to care, they cope better with distress and are more willing and able to give the utmost of themselves to their work. Prioritising kindness is not just the right thing for organisations to do, it offers a strategic advantage by affecting factors such as co-operation, information flow, safety, learning, innovation, commitment, motivation, retention and adaptability which all impact productivity, performance, and ultimately profitability. Both ethically and financially, it pays to be kind.

References:

[1] Gallup – Employee Engagement https://www.gallup.com/workplace/229424/employee-engagement.aspx [Accessed 24-04-21].

[2] Barnett, A. G., & Dobson, A. J. (2005). Excess in cardiovascular events on Mondays: a meta-analysis and prospective study. *Heart*, *91*(5), 612-612. doi: 10.1007/s10654-004-8783-6.

[3] Pryce-Jones, J. (2011). *Happiness at work: Maximizing your psychological capital for success*. Hoboken: John Wiley & Sons. doi: 10.1002/9780470666845.

[4] Accenture - Gender-balanced workforce by 2025. (2017). https://www.accenture.com/ca-en/company-news-release-balanced-workforce-2025 [Accessed 02-06-21].

[5] Zessin, U., Dickhäuser, O., & Garbade, S. (2015). The relationship between self-compassion and well-being: A meta-analysis. *Applied Psychology: Health and Well-Being*, *7*(3), 340-364. doi: 10.1111/aphw.12051.

[6] Eldor, L. (2018). Public service sector: The compassionate workplace—The effect of compassion and stress on employee engagement, burnout, and performance. *Journal of Public Administration Research and Theory*, *28*(1), 86-103. doi: 10.5465/AMBPP.2017.10296abstract.

[7] Edmondson, A. C., & Lei, Z. (2014). Psychological safety: The history, renaissance, and future of an interpersonal construct. *Annual Review of Organizational Psychology and Organizational Behavior.1*(1), 23-43. doi: 10.1146/annurev-orgpsych-031413-091305.

[8] International Air Transport Association (2019) World Air Transport Statistics. Available at https://www.iata.org/contentassets/a686ff624550453e8bf0c9b3f7f0ab26/wats-2019-mediakit.pdf [accessed 10-06-21] .

[9] Rogovsky, N., & Sims, E. (20026). *Corporate success through people: making international labour standards work for you*. Geneva: International Labour Organization & Academic Foundation.

[10] Li, Y., Zhang, J., & Perc, M. (2018). Effects of compassion on the evolution of cooperation in spatial social dilemmas. *Applied Mathematics and Computation*, *320*, 437-443. doi: 10.1016/j.amc.2017.10.002.

[11] Apker, J., Propp, K. M., Ford, W. S. Z., & Hofmeister, N. (2006). Collaboration, credibility, compassion, and coordination: professional nurse communication skill sets in health care team interactions. *Journal of professional nursing*, *22*(3), 180-189. doi: 10.1016/j.profnurs.2006.03.002.

[12] Wieseke, J., Geigenmüller, A., & Kraus, F. (2012). On the role of empathy in customer-employee interactions. *Journal of service research*, *15*(3), 316-331. doi: 10.1177/1094670512439743.

[13] Scott, B. A., Colquitt, J. A., Paddock, E. L., & Judge, T. A. (2010). A daily investigation of the role of manager empathy on employee well-being. *Organizational Behavior and Human Decision Processes*, *113*(2), 127-140. doi: 10.1016/j.obhdp.2010.08.001.

[14] Grant, A. M., Dutton, J. E., & Rosso, B. D. (2008). Giving commitment: Employee support programs and the prosocial sensemaking process. *Academy of management journal*, *51*(5), 898-918. doi: 10.5465/AMJ.2008.34789652.

[15] Kanov, J. M., Maitlis, S., Worline, M. C., Dutton, J. E., Frost, P. J., & Lilius, J. M. (2004). Compassion in organizational life. *American Behavioral Scientist*, *47*(6), 808-827. doi: 10.1177/0002764203260211.

Chapter 9
Kindness for Enhanced Leadership

A single act of kindness throws out roots in all directions, and the roots spring up and make new trees. -
Amelia Earheart

Until recently, for university students studying business, kindness was perceived as the least essential quality in a leader[1]. The COVID-19 pandemic has helped to shift perspectives and kindness is now understood to be vitally important if leaders are to be successful[2&3].

Leaders need to achieve desired results whilst minimising bad outcomes. These tend to be defined by quantitative data, such as sales figures, share prices, projects completed successfully, or votes gained. The ability to achieve these hard quantitative results depends on a leader's ability to achieve, much more difficult-to-measure, soft qualitative outcomes/results.

Research reveals successful leaders have followers who feel purposeful, important and valued[4,5&6]. The followers also feel they belong to their team, are proud to be members and feel loyal to the team and its leader[7,8&9]. Furthermore, successful leaders make the people they lead feel committed to, and motivated by, common goals as well as making everybody feel safe within the team or organisation[10&11].

Leaders operating in high-stakes and dangerous situations are particularly aware of how achieving the desired quantitative outcomes depends on realising the softer, qualitative outcomes first. Simon Frusher, a former officer in the British Army and now a vice-president at the investment bank Morgan Stanley, states:

> "The quality of the relationships, the level of trust and the strength of the bond between people are important because they determine how well people work together. In tough situations you need to be able to work quickly and seamlessly together and for that, everybody needs to trust and care for each other. We all have to know that we have each other's back, and that we are going all out together. It is this *espirt de corps*, this togetherness, this kinship that is essential for operational efficiency and success. And that is based on relationships you build through spending time with your guys, humour, respect and caring for each other. As a leader you have to know your guys and care for them".
>
> (Simon Frusher[12])

Kindness in a leader is a catalyst for creating conditions for optimal performance. As a leader, when you are kind, you signal that you are kin - that you are family. You demonstrate that the needs and success of those you lead are as important, or more important, than your own. As Simon Senek demonstrates in *Leaders Eat Last*, successful leaders put their followers first[13]. When people understand their leader truly cares, several things happen. Firstly, a powerful bond is created between follower and leader, because basic human needs for feeling safe, valued, and purposeful are met. This leads people to be intrinsically motivated to give the very best of themselves. Secondly, people feel they belong, and tribal instincts are activated, which engenders a strong commitment to the group or team and its goals. Thirdly, there is greater resilience, because the negative impact of distressing emotions on performance is minimised as people are better able to acknowledge, contain, make sense of, share, process and resolve emotional distress. Kindness therefore makes a group tougher and stronger. Fourthly, followers are kinder among themselves, amplifying the beneficial effects of a leader's kindness among the group.

Being kind as a leader is more than asking people in a perfunctory way, "how do you feel?". You have got to genuinely care. You genuinely care by being committed to promoting the wellbeing of those you lead and preventing or reducing their suffering. This means understanding what people want and need. It means communicating through language and actions that you want the best for them. That is, you want them as individuals to succeed and that you are there for them. It also entails being transparent and honest, taking responsibility for the welfare of your people, and, if necessary, taking tough and difficult action to ensure it.

When leaders fail, the quality of the bond, the depth of the trust, and the strength of the connection between leader and followers weakens. Followers reserve some, or a lot, of their intellectual and emotional capital in order to look out for themselves. Additionally, the ambitions and motives of the leader and followers can slip out of alignment, meaning performance, particularly in challenging situations, becomes suboptimal.

When leaders prioritise kindness towards all of their followers, like metal ions aligning when placed in a magnetic field, leaders and followers become aligned in their desire and determination to succeed together. People give their utmost and bring all of their strengths, experiences, commitment and humanity to bear in pursuit of the common goals. Kindness fuels extraordinary commitment and performance, as leaders benefit from the undiluted and collective, intellectual, creative, emotional and physical resources of their followers. Kindness is important if leaders are to be successful[2&3], and many business schools are now starting to teach this[14].

References

[1] Holt, S., & Marques, J. (2012). Empathy in leadership: Appropriate or misplaced? An empirical study on a topic that is asking for attention. *Journal of business ethics*, *105*(1), 95-105. doi: 10.1007/s10551-011-0951-5.

[2] Baker, W. F., & O'Malley, M. (2008). *Leading with kindness: How good people consistently get superior results*. New York: AMACOM.

[3] Haskins, G., Thomas, M., & Johri, L. (Eds.). (2018). *Kindness in Leadership*. New York: Routledge.

[4] Csikszentmihalyi, M. (2004). *Good business: Leadership, flow, and the making of meaning*. Penguin.

[5] Mai, R. P., & Akerson, A. (2003). *The leader as communicator: Strategies and tactics to build loyalty, focus effort, and spark creativity*. New York: AMACOM.

[6] Sullivan, E. J., & Garland, G. (2010). *Practical leadership and management in nursing*. London: Pearson Education.

[7] Bass, B. M., & Riggio, R. E. (2006). *Transformational leadership*. Hove: Psychology Press.

[8] Goleman, D., Boyatzis, R. E., & McKee, A. (2013). *Primal leadership: Unleashing the power of emotional intelligence*. Harvard Business Press.

[9] Maddock, S. (2012). Public leadership: motivated by values not bonuses. *International Journal of Leadership in Public Services*. *23*(8), 112-120. doi: 10.1108/17479881211279986.

[10] Riggio, R. E., & Reichard, R. J. (2008). The emotional and social intelligences of effective leadership. *Journal of Managerial Psychology*, *23*(2), 169-185. doi: 10.1108/02683940810850808.

[11] Palmer, B., Walls, M., Burgess, Z., & Stough, C. (2001). Emotional intelligence and effective leadership. *Leadership and Organization Development Journal*, *22*(1), 5-10. doi: 10.1108/01437730110380174.

[12] Frusher, A. (2017) personal communication, 22nd September, 2020.

[13] Sinek, S (2014) *Leaders Eat Last*. London: Penguin.

[14] Cohen, M. A. (2012). Empathy in business ethics education. *Journal of business ethics education*, 9, 359-375. doi: 10.5840/jbee2012918.

Chapter 10

The Dangers, Critiques and Challenges of Kindness

Twitter exchange:

Kindness is not debatable - *Gary Vaynerchuck*
But it is seen as a weakness - *Jaap Hoeve*
By weak people. - *Gary Vaynerchuck*

The danger in promoting kindness by emphasising the many advantages of kindness is that it can lead to selfish motivations for being kind. If the inherent goodness of kindness is forgotten and there is an obvious ulterior motive behind seemingly kind action, the danger is that kindness becomes seen as fake, with no real human currency, leading to cynicism and wariness. It would be ironic, sad and damaging if the promotion of kindness backfires, causing not more but less kindness to flow. Awareness of the risk that fake kindness poses serves to mitigate this risk, but greater protection comes from the sensitivity we all have to insincerity when it comes to kindness.

Two critiques are levelled at the promotion of kindness: that in many situations kindness is irrelevant, and in others, it is inappropriate or harmful. For example, it might argued that the kindness of an air traffic controller or surgeon when on the job is irrelevant since what determines successful outcomes are technical skills above all else. It is not wise, however, to relegate the role of kindness to complete unimportance. Surgeons being kind to patients improves clinical outcomes[1&2] and can reduce the risk of medical errors[3]. For air traffic controllers, there are cognitive benefits and positive implications for safety when they work in a kind environment and communicate with colleagues and pilots kindly[4].

Kindness, it is also suggested, is inappropriate or harmful in many management, leadership and negotiation settings as it may lead to a perception of weakness, or an attempt to mask incompetence. These perceptions are due to confusing kindness with being submissive or fawning. One can negotiate, manage and lead while combining self-assurance, strength and kindness, which will often lead to enhanced results[5&6]. When negotiation partners, employees and followers see that you are genuinely concerned with their needs, the quality of interactions improve, solutions are facilitated, and mutually beneficial and successful outcomes are more likely to be achieved[7&8].

The concern that kindness may be a façade, or an excuse for ineptitude and poor performance, again rests on a false understanding of kindness. If someone is attempting to hide poor performance by being nice, that is not kindness. Genuine kindness requires honesty, transparency and willingness to do what is possible to reduce suffering and promote wellbeing for everyone.

Leaving aside concerns about the potential dangers and critiques of kindness, even when we want to be kind, it can be difficult. The difficulties include believing somebody does not deserve to be treated kindly or perhaps believing that the kind action will be of no consequence and is therefore pointless. A further potential difficulty is not knowing how to be kind in an effective way or simply not having the time, money or other resources available with which to be kind. Additionally, we can experience emotional hurdles to being kind, such as feeling overwhelmed or whenever our threat system is overly activated. When we feel stressed, anxious or rushed, even in the face of an obvious need to be kind, it can be remarkably easy to withhold kindness. This was demonstrated in a social psychology experiment in which trainee Christian ministers were individually asked to hurry from one building to another where they would have to a deliver a sermon. On the way, each man passed an actor slumped in an alleyway moaning with pain and coughing. Only ten per cent of the men stopped to offer help, even though they were about to deliver a sermon on "The Good Samaritan"[9]. In a similar way, the pressure of meeting targets and the fear of adverse repercussions was identified as a key reason for the Stafford Hospital scandal in the UK, in which medical staff failed to give patients assistance with eating and left them without water and in soiled bedclothes for unacceptably long periods[10]. Arguably, the fundamental emotional challenge for potential givers of kindness is a reliance on empathy to fuel kind acts. The problem is that empathy is fickle, and in its absence, kindness is withheld even where there is an obvious need for it. As Paul Bloom, professor of psychology at Yale University argues in his book *Against Empathy*[11], kindness should be driven by rational decisions and information, not feelings of emotional resonance with others, or the lack of such feeling.

It is not just potential givers of kindness that face challenges. Potential receivers have challenges too that limit their ability to receive kindness. They may perceive receiving kindness from others as patronising. They may have concerns that accepting kindness could signal that they are needy, or require help because of a lack of skill, ability, competency or smarts. Alternatively, they may worry the kindness may not be genuine, that they are being "softened up" and, that by accepting the kindness, they will be making themselves vulnerable and morally indebted. None of these responses are necessarily always unwarranted, but equally, in the face of genuine kindness they represent challenges that need to be overcome if kindness is to flow.

So, kindness is not always so easy or straight-forward. The three Cs can help us overcome some of these kindness challenges; calm, connect and consider. By calming down and reducing activation of the threat system, by for instance, slowing down our breathing, we can better assess the situation we find ourselves in and, if appropriate, take kind action. Calming down also helps us to connect at a human level by listening, learning, finding common ground, and if necessary, using our imaginations to understand the world as experienced by others. When we feel no empathy, or emotional compunction to be kind, taking time to consider the situation helps us identify whether there may be a good, objective and rational reason to be kind. This is particularly relevant to applying kindness at a collective and societal level, as is discussed in the next chapter. Given the challenges, danger and possible critiques of promoting kindness, it is imperative that we adopt an intelligent and considered approach, so that genuine and effective kindness can flourish.

References

[1] Cochrane et al., (2019). A culture of compassion: How timeless principles of kindness and empathy become powerful tools for confronting today's most pressing healthcare challenges. In *Healthcare management forum* (Vol. 32, No. 3, pp. 120-127). doi: 10.1177/0840470419836240.

[2] Kelley et al., (2014). The influence of the patient-clinician relationship on healthcare outcomes: a systematic review & meta-analysis of RCTs. *PloS one* 9, e94207. doi: 10.1371/journal.pone.0094207.

[3] Youngson (2012). *Time to care: How to love your patients and your job*. New Zealand: Rebelheart Publishers.

[4] Li, W. C., Chen, H. C., & Wu, F. E. (2000). Human errors in the cockpit and accidents prevention strategies from cockpit resources management perspective. In 19th DASC. 19th Digital Avionics Systems Conference. Proceedings (Cat. No. 00CH37126) (Vol. 2, pp. 5D1-1). IEEE.

[5] Baker, W.F. and O'Malley, M., (2008). *Leading with kindness: How good people consistently get superior results.* New York: AMACOM.

[6] Gilbert, P. (2015). Negotiating in the world of mixed beliefs and value systems: A compassion-focused model. In *Handbook of International Negotiation* (pp. 261-277). New York: Springer.

[7] Miller, K. I. (2007). Compassionate communication in the workplace: Exploring processes of noticing, connecting, and responding. *Journal of Applied Communication Research*, *35*(3), 223-245. doi: 10.1080/00909880701434208.

[8] Worline, M., & Dutton, J. E. (2017). *Awakening compassion at work: The quiet power that elevates people and organizations*. Oakland: Berrett-Koehler Publishers.

[9] Darley, J.M. and Batson, C.D., (1973). "From Jerusalem to Jericho": A study of situational and dispositional variables in helping behavior. *Journal of personality and social psychology*, *27*(1),100-110. doi: 10.1037/h0034449.

[10] HMSO (2013). Report of the Mid Staffordshire NHS Foundation Trust Public Inquiry: executive summary. Available at https://www.gov.uk/government/publications/report-of-the-mid-staffordshire-nhs-foundation-trust-public-inquiry [Accessed 14-06-21].

[11] Bloom, P. (2017). *Against empathy: The case for rational compassion*. New York: Random House.

Chapter 11

Kindness in the World: Politics, Economics, Cities and the Environment

Unexpected kindness is the most powerful, least costly, and most underrated agent of human change. - Bob Kerrey

The overarching, global, long-term challenge we face is how we and future generations can live together on Earth safely, sustainably and harmoniously. Succeeding in this will require us to overcome challenges in our politics, our economies, our cities and how we treat the environment: challenges which are central causes of much of our present day, and likely future, suffering.

We live in times of increasingly fractious politics[1]. The rise of identity and far-right politics, nationalism and a diminished sense of community reduces understanding among people across society. This promotes distrust, prejudice and anger, which can lead to aggression and violence[2&3]. In some parts of the world, authoritarian regimes appear to be increasing their grip on power and deploying it ruthlessly against those asking for freedom of political expression and human rights[4].

Economic inequality and poverty are other, related, sources of human suffering. The world as a whole is, in theory, getting richer, but the way wealth is generated comes at a cost to the environment and social cohesion. Since 2000, there has been a doubling of those who live with food insecurity in the USA. Nearly 20 per cent of Americans do not know if they will have enough to eat day by day[5]. At a global level, two thirds of the world's population is living on less than 10 international dollars* a day, with research indicating that by 2030, two thirds of the world will be living I n fragile and conflict-affected economies[6].

Economic fragility is paralleled by the increasing vulnerability of many essential support systems[7]. Food supply chains, water supply, transportation infrastructure and the provision of healthcare, social care and education are increasingly overburdened by rising populations and urbanisation in many parts of the world[8]. Ever bigger cities result in higher concentrations of pollution and waste, not only adversely affecting our health but also adding to the already onerous list of burdens that our industrial processes and fossil-fuel burning, plastic-ridden, consumeristic society place on the environment[9]. If we continue to take insufficient action to redress environmental challenges, we store up ever greater dangers and suffering for ourselves and future generations.

Many of the challenges and much of the suffering in the world are of our own making and are set to increase. An understanding of the individual and societal behaviours that lead to such man-made problems and suffering may help reduce them.

* An international dollar is a made-up unit of currency that would buy a comparable amount of goods and services a US dollar would buy in the USA. Therefore, 10 international dollars is the value that 10 US dollars would buy in the USA.

There are two types of man-made suffering. Firstly, there is *inflicted* suffering caused directly by human action and intended to damage, hurt or kill; such as suffering due to bullying, abuse, violence and wars. Secondly, there is *preventable* suffering that occurs because action to prevent it has *not* been taken. This includes suffering caused by political decisions and socio-economic systems that mean available resources that *could* fund access to healthcare, education, housing and improvements in safety are allocated elsewhere.

Man-made suffering can be understood as a combined result of firstly, human psychology, and the secondly, socio-economic systems and power structures in society[10]. Understanding the first is most helpful in making sense of inflicted suffering and the second in making sense of preventable suffering.

The psychological factors that account for people's willingness to inflict suffering include perceiving themselves as separate, different and better than others and failing to have empathy[3]. When we do not sense any connection between the common humanity in others and our own selves, it becomes easy to disregard them. Furthermore, if we perceive others to represent a threat, it makes it easier to also want to be rid of them[11].

Inflicting suffering on others can also be driven by an unhealthy relationship with our own pain and fear. Many of us have significant resistance to being emotionally vulnerable[12]. We avoid engaging with difficult emotions and the thoughts and memories that can underpin them. When we fail to acknowledge and work through our pain and fears, there is an increased likelihood of us behaving in ways that cause pain and fear in others[13].

Insight into the causes of preventable suffering requires an understanding of the way society is organised and functions. Nobody explicitly states that the suffering of starving children, migrants drowning at sea, or the homeless family is desirable or acceptable, and nobody individually directly causes it. Nonetheless, measures that are both realistic and feasible are not taken to the extent required to have lasting impact on preventing or eliminating the suffering.

So, why is this? Firstly, the suffering is unseen or unreported and so occurs unnoticed by the majority in society. Secondly, the suffering is noticed, but considered, incorrectly, unavoidable with nothing that can be done to prevent it. Thirdly, the suffering is considered the fault of those suffering, which serves to inhibit action to reduce the suffering especially in societies which place great value on individual responsibility, competitiveness and freedom of choice.

Numerous scholars have argued that deliberate inaction by those in society with greater socio-economic and political power is a key factor in sustaining preventable suffering in the world which disproportionately affects the poor[14]. This is because of the benefits of cheap labour costs, services and goods that those at the bottom of the socio-economic scale provide.

An inevitable consequence for many living at the lower end of the socio-economic scale is more precarious life circumstances, which not only keeps them in low-paid work but also means that they face a greater risk of suffering through economic, educational, health and personal hardships[15&16]. Therefore, the same precarious life circumstances of the poor that are a cause of increased risks of suffering for them, also underpin an economic advantage for others in society.

Can encouraging and prioritising kindness really help to reduce and resolve the problem of man-made suffering and the problems in our politics, economics, cities and the environment?

Prioritising kindness weakens the psychological drivers of inflicted suffering. Kindness works against separateness and disconnect, creating instead connection, empathy and a sense of shared humanity. Kindness encourages us to take rational action to reduce suffering. Kindness also facilitates a healthier engagement with pain and fear. When we are kind to ourselves and others, it becomes safer and easier to be vulnerable, allowing us to admit, express and work through emotional pain and fear.

At a societal level, kindness spreads rapidly through social networks[17], and has a multiplicative effect[18&19]. According to systems theory, only a small proportion of society needs to act with more kindness for a threshold and tipping point to be reached that causes all of society to change[20,21&22]. An upsurge in kindness could have a substantial impact on reducing the factors that enable preventable suffering to occur.

As a society, prioritising kindness in our politics, in how we run our economies, our cities and how we treat the environment, can serve as an over-arching strategy for creating a safer, fairer, more harmonious, cleaner and prosperous world.

Kindness and politics may not seem natural bedfellows, yet if the purpose of government and politics is ultimately to promote societal wellbeing and reduce suffering, then kindness should be at the heart of politics and government. For example, strategies for reducing social inequalities and homelessness can be framed as a commitment to kindness. In the UK, the current piecemeal approach to dealing with homelessness is inefficient and costly. It would be kinder, more economical and have greater impact if there were a co-ordinated, national, strategic approach to homelessness. Achieving this, however, would require an upsurge of political will, which a strong commitment to kindness could unleash.

Promoting kindness in cities could be especially impactful. There is scientific evidence that kindness improves the wellbeing of both giver and receiver in many different contexts[23,24,25&26]. Therefore, cities could implement evidence-based policies, regulations and incentives for businesses and social services to encourage kindness. Applying insights from behavioural science, alongside education campaigns and social advertising, could be utilised to do so. Facilitating opportunities for volunteering could also serve as an especially accessible and practical way of facilitating the giving and receiving of kindness.

Finally, kindness is relevant to our relationship with the environment. Ensuring that we do not cause further irreversible damage to natural resources and ecosystems is being kind to ourselves and future generations. To ensure our children inherit a viable planet, more concerted efforts are needed to reduce pollution now[27]. Mustering increased collective will to take more measures to better protect our environment can, once again, be framed as a commitment to kindness.

As we progress further into the 21st century, we face growing threats, which stem largely from our own behaviour as humans towards each other and the planet. The psychological and sociological factors that cause these behaviours continue undimmed. Continual developments in automation, artificial intelligence, biotechnology and military warfare mean the power at our disposal to control the environment and fellow human beings is rapidly increasing. Unless we get a handle on the malign tendencies in our human nature, we risk facing situations in which incredibly powerful technology combines with the dark side of humanity. The outcomes do not bear thinking about. Indeed, researchers at the Future of Humanity Institute at Oxford University, predict that over the next one hundred years humanity faces a one in six probability of "existential catastrophe" caused by AI gone wrong, an engineered pandemic or other man-made cause[28,29&30].

We need everyone to contribute to a collective effort to ensure the better angels of our human[31&32] nature prevail and predominate. We may be the last generation with the possibility of saving the world from irrevocable damage and saving humanity from its own destructive tendencies.

The risks of failing to embed compassion, care, respect, dignity, equality and justice into our operating systems as individuals, communities and as a global society are too big and urgent for any of us to hold back from making the case for kindness with the utmost boldness and courage. As argued in the next and final chapter, each of us needs to be willing, when necessary, to be assertive, and fierce in promoting kindness.

References

[1] Ipsos Mori Social Research Institute. (2017). BBC Global Survey: A world divided? Available at https://www.ipsos.com/ipsos-mori/en-uk/bbc-global-survey-world-divided [Accessed 22-06-21].

[2] Burnett, J. (2013). Britain: Racial violence and the politics of hate. *Race & class*, *54*(4), 5-21. doi: 10.117/030639681347 5981 [Accessed 22-10-20].

[3] Taylor, M., Holbrook, D., & Currie, P. M. (Eds.). (2013). *Extreme right wing political violence and terrorism*. London: Bloomsbury.

[4] Yale Macmillian Centre, (2020) *Democracy and Rise of Authoritarianism in COVID-19 World* [webinar]. Available at https://www.youtube.com/watch?v=weWzfa-52Ew&feature=youtu.be [Accessed 23-06-21].

5 Myers, C. A., Mire, E. F., & Katzmarzyk, P. T. (2020). Trends in Adiposity and Food Insecurity Among US Adults. *JAMA network open*, 3(8), e2012767-e2012767. doi:10.1001/jamanetworkopen.2020.12767.

6 World Bank (2020). *Fragility and Conflict: On the Front Lines of the Fight Against Poverty* Report. Available at https://openknowledge.worldbank.org/bitstream/handle/10 986/33324/9781464815409.pdf [Accessed 20-06-21].

7 Maynard, A. (2001) Ethics and health care 'underfunding'. *Journal of Medical Ethics*, 27:223-227. doi: 10.1136/jme.27.4.223.

8 Pettinger, T. (2017). *Impact of rising population in the UK*. Economics Help. https://www.economicshelp.org/blog/11031/uk-economy/impact-of-rising-population-in-the-uk/ [accessed 16-06-21].

9 Hubbe, A., & Hubbe, M. (2019) *Current Climate Change and the Future of Life on the Planet*. Front. Young Minds. 7:37. doi: 10.3389/frym.2019.00037.

10 Gilbert, P. (2017). *Living like crazy*. York: Annwyn House.

11 Staub, E. (1989). *The roots of evil: The origins of genocide and other group violence*. Cambridge University Press.

12 Brown, B. (2006). Shame resilience theory: A ground theory study on women and shame. *Families in Society*, *87*(1), 43-52. doi: 10.1606/1044-3894.3483.

13 Abramsky, T., Watts, C. H., Garcia-Moreno, C., Devries, K., Kiss, L., Ellsberg, M., ... & Heise, L. (2011). What factors are associated with recent intimate partner violence? Findings from the WHO multi-country study on women's health and domestic violence? Findings from the WHO multi-country study on women's health and domestic violence. *BMC Public Health*, *11*(1), 109. doi: 10.1186/1471-2458-11-109.

[14] Pogge, T. (2005). Severe poverty as a violation of negative duties. *Ethics & International Affairs*, *19*(1), 55-83. doi: 10.1111/j.1747-7093.2005.tb00490.x.

[15] Blunt, G. D. (2015). Is global poverty a crime against humanity?. *International Theory*, *7*(3), 539-571. doi: 10.1017/S1752971915000123.

[16] Pogge, T. (2005b). World poverty and human rights. *Ethics & international affairs*, *19*(1), 1-7. doi: 10.1111/j.1747-7093.2005.tb00484.x.

[17] Chancellor, J., Margolis, S., Jacobs Bao, K., & Lyubomirsky, S. (2018). Everyday prosociality in the workplace: The reinforcing benefits of giving, getting, and glimpsing. *Emotion*, 18(4), 507. doi: 10.1037/emo0000321.

[18] Fowler, J. H., & Christakis, N. A. (2010). Cooperative behavior cascades in human social networks. *Proceedings of the National Academy of Sciences*, *107*(12), 5334-5338. doi: 10.1073/pnas.0913149107.

[19] Rowland, L. (2018). Kindness: Society's golden chain. *The Psychologist*, *31*, 30-35.

[20] Buckley W, Schwandt D.(2008) An introduction to "Society as a complex adaptive system". Emergence: Complexity and Organization. 10(3), 86. doi: 10.emerg/10.17357.06e9a4b2212fd8b56de2bd2009e3a348.

[21] Oinas-kukkonen, H. (2010). Behavior change support systems: the next frontier for web science. In *in: Proceedings of the Web Science* April 26-27, 2010, Raleigh, NC, USA.

Available at https://www.researchgate.net/profile/Harri_Oinas-Kukkonen/publication/228953743_Behavior_change_supp ort_systems_The_next_frontier_for_web_science/links/0 2e7e52838f73a7c90000000.pdf [Accessed 19-06-21].

[22] Trevillion, E. (2002). Systems theory and the commercial development process-towards an understanding of complex behaviour and change. In Guy, S. & Henneberry. J. (Eds.) *Development and Developers: perspectives on property*, Oxford: Blackwell Science 181-203.

[23] Casiday, R., Kinsman, E., Fisher, C., & Bambra, C. (2008). Volunteering and health: what impact does it really have. London: *Volunteering England, 9*(3), 1-13.

[24] Lyubomirsky, S., & Layous, K. (2013). How do simple positive activities increase well-being?. *Current directions in psychological science, 22*(1), 57-62. doi: 10.1177/0963721412469809.

[25] NCVO (2019) *Time Well Spent*. London NCVO. https://www.ncvo.org.uk/images/documents/policy_and_re search/volunteering/Volunteer-experience_Full-Report.pdf [Accessed 23-06-21].

[26] Curry, O. S., Rowland, L. A., Van Lissa, C. J., Zlotowitz, S., McAlaney, J., & Whitehouse, H. (2018). Happy to help? A systematic review and meta-analysis of the effects of performing acts of kindness on the well-being of the actor. *Journal of Experimental Social Psychology, 76*, 320-329. doi: 10.1016/j.jesp.2018.02.014.

[27] Eckstein, D., Künzel, V., Schäfer, L., & Winges, M. (2019). Global climate risk index 2020. Germanwatch. Available at: https://germanwatch. org/sites/germanwatch. org/files/20-2-01e% 20Global, 20. [Accessed 23-06-21].

[28] Ord, T. (2020). *The precipice: existential risk and the future of humanity*. London: Hachette Books.

[29] Future of Humanity Institute, University of Oxford (2020) Research. Available at https://www.fhi.ox.ac.uk/research/research-areas/ [Accessed 10-06-21].

[30] Bostrum, N (2019) The Vulnerable World Hypothesis. *Global Policy, 10*(4), 455-476. doi: 10.1111/1758-5899.12718.

[31] Lincoln, A (1861). Inaugural Address 4th March 1861. Available at https://avalon.law.yale.edu/19th_century/lincoln1.asp [accessed 10-06-21] The phrase "better angels of our human nature" comes from close of American president Abraham Lincoln inaugural address given just before the start of the American Civil War in which he sought to call both sides to peace: *We are not enemies, but friends. We must not be enemies. Though passion may have strained, it must not break our bonds of affection. The mystic chords of memory will swell when again touched, as surely they will be, by the better angels of our nature.*

[32] Pinker, S. (2012). *The Better Angels of Our Nature: A History of Violence and Humanity*. New York: Penguin.

Chapter 12

Intelligent, Courageous and Fierce Kindness

Enough words have been exchanged
Now at last let me see deeds!
Something useful should transpire...
So get on with it! - *Johann Wolfgang von Goethe*

This pocket guide to kindness summarises the many wide-ranging advantages that come with being kind. It arms you with what is currently, scientifically known about kindness, so that you can be a more knowledgeable and effective champion for it. This book is a call to action. I want to motivate and inspire you and others to do more to promote kindness. Prioritising kindness, as detailed in Chapter Eleven, is now more important and necessary than ever. However, being kind is not always easy. As is made clear in Chapter One, kindness should not be confused with simply being nice. Kindness is doing something that is exclusively intended to promote wellbeing or reduce or prevent suffering. Being kind *can* be simple and straightforward, but it can also be complicated, hard work, distressing and even scary, which is why kindness is not as prevalent as it could be.

If we, as individuals and organisations, are to succeed in being kinder we will, at times, need to be courageous, as well as intelligent and wise to reduce suffering and promote wellbeing.

A kind intention that is not underpinned by knowledge and intelligence can lead to actions that are, at best, ineffective and at worst, harmful. To illustrate this point, think of the potential for harm that exists if a person with no medical skill or knowledge attempts to help someone with a complex medical problem regardless of how well-intentioned they are.

Similarly, to be truly effective at reducing suffering and promoting wellbeing across our world demands that we apply wisdom. Human psychology is tricky and the way we have created social and economic systems and behave within these systems is complicated[1]. We need to better comprehend both what inhibits and what facilitates kindness in individuals, organisations and society. We need to understand how to best structure and redesign our systems as a society to foster greater kindness. We need more research into kindness and compassion to generate the required knowledge and understanding, as well as to generate the evidence base necessary to convince and guide people to take action. If we are to harness fully the power of kindness to improve our world, we must be organised and strategic. We also must apply the new knowledge of the science of kindness intelligently. To swap 'kindness' for the word 'peace', in paraphrasing a famous quote from Martin Luther King: *Those who love kindness need to learn to organise themselves as much as those who love and proclaim war[2].*

So, it is imperative that we apply knowledge and understanding of the science of kindness and develop an organised approach, if kindness is to be seriously scaled up across organisations and society. However, in many situations this alone will not be sufficient to ensure kindness prevails.

There are barriers to kindness that exist within ourselves. Being kind can be effortful, distressing and risky. Acting with kindness, or in this case specifically, compassion, means choosing to notice, confront and deal with suffering. Most of us resist leaning into suffering. It's distressing. It's hard. It requires courage.

As individuals, we cannot promote kindness without a willingness to grow our own capacities to be kind and to lead with kindness. This often demands personal growth. It can mean facing one's fears, vulnerabilities and past pain with acceptance, equanimity and even positivity[3]. Again, it's hard. It requires courage.

Leaders who are committed to implementing kindness as a guiding principle can still be met with scepticism, suspicion, and flak, especially in business. Other than Jeff Weiner, CEO of LinkedIn[4], it is hard to find business leaders reported as publicly championing kindness. This is in spite of the growing evidence of the importance of kindness for employee wellbeing[5] and its positive correlation with a firm's profitability[6]. Are they just not informed, do they not value kindness, or do they just not dare? If leaders are to initiate change and promote kindness, they need to know about the research, but above all, they need to be bold and courageous. Their courage in championing kindness is essential. This is because the single greatest potential driving force for transforming society and promoting kindness globally would be if the corporate world were to genuinely embrace the ethic of kindness. This would involve ensuring that a fundamental purpose of business is the promotion of wellbeing and the reduction of suffering among the broadest possible range of stakeholders.

Finally, a commitment to kindness also entails identifying, and attempting to stop suffering. This might mean calling out unethical behaviour, whistleblowing, confronting ignorance, prejudice and vested interests and taking a stand against wrongdoing. Those who advocate for kindness in such situations are often met with resistance and frequently threatened. It therefore comes with risks, especially when those identified as responsible for causing, contributing to, or condoning suffering are powerful and not willing to enact change. In such situations, the easiest and safest path is to withdraw and turn away. If, however, one does not want to be cowed into submission and is resolute about bringing positive change and more kindness into the world, then one has to fight and stand firm in the face of the forces thwarting kindness. Irish statesman and philosopher Edmund Burke is famously attributed with writing "All that is necessary for the triumph of evil is for good men to do nothing"[7]. If we want an upsurge in societal kindness, we all have to play a part. At times, it is likely that the only effective alternative to doing nothing, is to be fierce, radical and assertive in upholding the need for kindness.

Novelist Raghu Karnad recounts how British philosopher Bertrand Russell wrote a manifesto appealing to logic and reasoning, concluding that the only way to ensure a safe future for mankind was to renounce war[8]. It was signed, shortly after the end of the Second World War, by Einstein and numerous atomic scientists, almost all of whom were Nobel Laureates. Einstein and his fellow scientists recognised, however, that humans do not operate rationally and that even if logic dictated that war must be renounced, logic alone would not determine human behaviour. In order to change minds and hearts, and shift behaviour, Einstein argued, "there must be added that deep power of emotion"[8].

Einstein's insight is as relevant today as it was in 1947. The risk of nuclear war is no longer the foremost threat on our minds, but humanity, as discussed in Chapter Eleven, continues to face significant perils, and endure considerable suffering – all as a direct result of man's behaviour toward his fellow beings. It is worth underscoring that it is predominantly *men's* and not women's behaviour that causes the risks and suffering for all. A significant strand of the solution to ending man-made risk and suffering is therefore the much needed, continued rise of women in politics, big business and other arenas of power and influence, together with increased gender equality globally.

So, rational arguments alone will not make humanity more kind. We need the power of emotion to change us. Who will provide the emotional push that, according to Einstein, is necessary if we are to evolve as a society? This is where you and I come into play. Each of us can commit to being kinder. When we are kind to others, we spread the positive emotions that are frequently associated with the receiving and giving of kindness. As research demonstrates, each kind act results in a ripple of positive emotion, which spreads rapidly through a social network[9&10]. If enough of us, as individuals, prioritise kindness in our interactions and spheres of influence, together these ripples of positivity connect, building up into a much more powerful wave of emotion capable of shifting social norms, bringing about lasting change, and widespread cultural and moral evolution.

References

[1] Gilbert, P. (2017). *Living Like Crazy* (2nd Revised edition). York: Annwyn House.

[2] Peace Alliance (2020) Inspirational quotes. Available at https://peacealliance.org/tools-education/peace-inspirational-quotes/ [Accessed 30-06-21].

[3] Quirin, M., Kent, M., Boksem, M. A., & Tops, M. (2015). Integration of negative experiences: A neuropsychological framework for human resilience. *Behavioral and Brain Sciences*, 38. doi: 10.1017/S0140525X14001666.

4Wharton (2018) *LinkedIn's Jeff Weiner: How Compassion Builds Better Companies.* [Blogpost] Knowledge@Wharton 17th May 2018. Available at https://knowledge.wharton.upenn.edu/article/linkedin-ceo-how-compassion-can-build-a-better-company/ [Accessed 15-06-21].

5 Scott, B. A., Colquitt, J. A., Paddock, E. L., & Judge, T. A. (2010). A daily investigation of the role of manager empathy on employee well-being. *Organizational Behavior and Human Decision Processes, 113*(2), 127–140. doi: 10.1016/j.obhdp.2010.08.001.

6 Sisodia, R., Sheth, J., & Wolfe, D. (2014). *Firms of Endearment: How World-Class Companies Profit from Passion and Purpose.* London: Pearson FT Press.

7 Edmund Burke, Thoughts on the Cause of the Present Discontents 82-83 (1770) In (Liberty Fund ed. 1999)z *Select Works of Edmund Burke*, vol. 1, p. 146 Available via http://www.openculture.com/2016/03/edmund-burkeon-in-action.html [Accessed 14-06-2021].

8 Karnar, R. (2020) The experience of Covid-19 shows how easily catastrophe can befall our species. *The Guardian.* 28th August Available at https://www.theguardian.com/commentisfree/2020/aug/29/covid-19-catastrophe [Accessed 16-06-21].

9 Chancellor, J., Margolis, S., Jacobs Bao, K., & Lyubomirsky, S. (2018). Everyday prosociality in the workplace: The reinforcing benefits of giving, getting, and glimpsing. *Emotion, 18*(4), 507. doi: 10.1037/emo0000321.

10 Fowler, J. H., & Christakis, N. A. (2010). Cooperative behavior cascades in human social networks. *Proceedings of the National Academy of Sciences, 107*(12), 5334-5338. doi: org/10.1073/pnas.0913149107.

Notes

Suggestions for How to be Kind

Suggestions for individuals

- Send an unprovoked 'thank you' text
- Be aware of opportunities where you can help
- Ask if you can help with something
- Reconnect with someone you haven't seen in a long time
- Give a gift to a friend or colleague without there being an occasion
- Make a donation to a good cause
- Invite someone else to join you in completing a kind act
- Thank someone who has made a difference in your life
- Get to know your neighbours
- Learn the name of someone you see regularly
- Give recognition to someone who rarely receives recognition
- Give someone a genuine compliment
- Strike up a conversation with a stranger
- Choose words with positive intentions when speaking
- Think, speak, and act with kindness.
- When you encounter someone, let your first thoughts be 'What kind words can I say to this person and what kind things can I do?'
- Listen to those who need someone to listen to them, it is a great act of kindness.

Suggestions for teams and organisations

- Monitoring and listening to colleagues, checking in on them
- Unique rituals and mementos when co-workers are suffering specifically tailored to them e.g collage with flowers
- Quotation whiteboard with kind quote of the day
- Updating company website with kind stories and messages
- Worker nomination awards for kind act of the week or month
- Adopt a charity for the year to contribute to and encourage workers to take part
- Create a 'compliment box' where workers can write complimentary messages
- Find every opportunity to recognise and thank colleagues for their work
- Buy recyclable products
- Recycling printer cartridges
- Sharing commute with co-workers
- Walk or cycle to work
- Plants and flowers in the workplace

Suggestions for leaders

- Set an example: be kind and be aware that you are a role model for followers
- Remember how you liked to be treated when you were a follower and act in the same way as a leader
- Take a personal interest in people, ask how they are
- Write personal notes to employees, that are unique and thanking them
- Share some of your weaknesses, it helps to build empathy in your followers
- Recognise and celebrate the success of others
- Help rather than blame
- Be clear on goals and expectations
- Be curious rather than defensive, be open to ideas
- Give constructive feedback to followers
- Be aware of your biases towards followers and aim to minimise them
- Find common ground in your relationships with followers
- Make inclusive decisions so you can consider the voices of followers

Some of these suggestions have been adapted from: Burmester & Lindsey (2020) *Be kind, a year of kindness, one week at a* time; Worline & Dutton (2017) *Awakening Compassion at Work'*; KindnessUK.com, WorkHuman.com and CareyNieuwhof.com

Further Reading

Baker, W. F., & O'Malley, M. (2008). *Leading with kindness: How good people consistently get superior results.* New York: AMACOM.

Ballatt, J., & Campling, P & Maloney, C. (2020). *Intelligent kindness: Rehabilitating the Welfare State.* Cambridge University Press.

Bregman, R. (2020). *Humankind A Hopeful History.* Bloomsbury.

Ferrucci, P. (2016). *The power of kindness: The unexpected benefits of leading a compassionate life.* Penguin.

Gilbert, P. (2009). *The Compassionate Mind.* Robinson.

Hamilton, D. R. (2017). *The Five Side Effects of Kindness: This Book Will Make You Feel Better, Be Happier & Live Longer.*Hay House UK Limited.

Haskins, G., Thomas, M., & Johri, L. (Eds.). (2018). *Kindness in Leadership.* Routledge.

McCullough, M, (2020). *The Kindness of Strangers How a Selfish Ape Invented a New Moral Code.* Oneworld.

Neff, K. (2021). *Fierce Self-compassion.* Penguin.

Kraft, H. (2020). *Deep Kindness.* Tiller Press.

Phillips, A., & Taylor, B. (2009). *On Kindness.* Macmillan.

Ricard, M. (2015). *Altruism: The power of compassion to change yourself and the world.* Hachette UK.

Sisodia, R., Wolfe, D., & Sheth, J. N. (2003). *Firms of endearment: How world-class companies profit from passion and purpose.* Prentice Hall.

Worline, M., & Dutton, J. E. (2017). *Awakening compassion at work: The quiet power that elevates people and organizations.* Berrett-Koehler Publishers.

Zaki, J. (2019). *The War for Kindness: Building empathy in a fractured world.* Broadway Books.

Acknowledgements

I would not have been able to complete this pocket guide without the help of many people. Jane Robins offered to be my co-author for a book on kindness two years ago. Whilst this joint project did not come to pass, her initial support was critical in getting me started writing. Steven Cooney is a fantastic colleague and research collaborator whose invaluable help enabled me to work much more efficiently. He has contributed significantly to identifying relevant research articles and typesetting the final manuscript. Leo Bonetto is an amazing brother-in-law and a highly-skilled designer and illustrator responsible for the design and illustration in the book. Emily Pyle has provided indispensable assistance in all manner of research, writing and administrative tasks which she always completes with speed and goodwill. She also gave much intelligently incisive feedback on my draft chapters. I am grateful to Gordon Asher for his proofreading. Bonny Hazelwood and Dr Sue Whiting gave especially valuable additional proofreading and editing, reading through with me the final draft, making improvements and ensuring the text was ready for recording. Andrew Bennet's expert guidance on vocal delivery was tremendously useful. My wonderful brother, Marcial Bóo, read through an initial draft and his comprehensive feedback was very instructive. Intellectually I am grateful to Dr Mark Coulson who first introduced me to wellbeing research and Professor Barbara Frederickson's keynote presentation at the World Congress in Positive in

Psychology in Philadelphia in 2011 seeded the idea that I too could research kindness. I subsequently undertook a course in Mindful Self-Compassion with Kristin Neff and Chris Germer, Mindfulness Teacher Training with Breathworks and attended numerous trainings organised by the Compassionate Mind Foundation. Indeed, I am particularly grateful for the pioneering work of Professor Paul Gilbert and the Compassion Focused Therapy community from whom I have learnt much. Presenting my own research on teaching self-compassion at The Science of Compassion Conference in San Francisco, organised by the Stanford Center for Compassion and Care Research founded by Dr Jim Doty, was an especially formative experience and gave me an opportunity to meet and learn from Professors Daniel Martin, Paul Ekman, Steven Porges and Daniel Batson and be inspired by the work of Ari Cowan, Dr Robin Youngson and the late Maurice Coles. Another intellectually formative time in the USA was attending, thanks to a scholarship, the University of California, Berkeley Greater Good Science Center Summer Camp for Educators, where I learnt more about compassion research from Professors Dachter Keltner and Emiliana Simon-Thomas, and the social and emotional aspects of learning from Dr Vicki Zakrzewski. Above all I am especially appreciative of Professor Jane Dutton, co-founder of the Center for Positive Organisations at the University of Michigan, for her on-going support and encouragement that I research compassion in organisations. In the UK, I have also been lucky to have so many academics researchers teach and guide me and must thank: Professor Michael Thomas; Professor Denis Mareschal; Professor Andie Tolmie; Dr Amy Remington; Dr Sveta Mayer; Professor Felecia Huppert; Dr Gillian Sandstrom; Dr Ace Simpson; Dr Theo Gilbert; Professor Nicola Martin; Dr Petia Sice; Dr Alan Watkins; Gay Haskins; Dr Juliet Galante; Professor Paul Dolan; Dr Jet Sanders and Adam Davidson. Furthermore, I wish to acknowledge the formative and enriching influence that Sandra Sinfield; Tom Burns; Anne Morris; Dr Anthony Basiel; Wende & Emil Bryden; Dr John & Barbara Lewington, Dr Guy Higby; Revd. Dr Nigel Rawlinson; Deirdre Wallace, Professor John Stephens, Professor Nicola Martin and the late Professor Neville Woolf and the late Professor Brostoff have had on me. I am also especially grateful to my doctoral supervisors Dr Pam Yeow and Professor Almuth McDowall in the Management and Occupational Psychology departments at Birkbeck. At the LSE, Kirsty McKenzie, Stef Hackney, Venitia Stoby and other members of the Student Wellbeing Service Team as well as Dr Clare Gordon, Dr Claudine Provencher and Dr Hong Lu OBE are wonderful colleagues. Fnally I'm grateful for the support and motivation given by Beatrice Tourot, Alejandra Oliver, Reetu Sood, Kai Kermani, Keith Elvin, Hilary Fraser, Ivan Newman, Kerry Pace, Aki Omote, Simon Akers, Steve Lindley, Taylor Damiani, Anand Patar, Yaobin Tong, PJ & Amy, Antoine & Diana, Siva & Izzy, Riz & Andrea, JP & Jenn, Emily & Matt, Victor & Ling, Pari & James, Oli, Julian, Brenda, Clemence, Jo, Assane, Tandis, Daisy and especially Xiaojing.

About the Author

Sebastian helps individuals, teams and organisations perform at their best by harnessing the power of kindness. He has had a permanent post with the London School of Economics and Political Science Student Wellbeing Service since 2010 advising and training students and staff. He founded Kindness Advantage Ltd. in 2015 to bring the benefits of kindness to corporate and public sector clients.

Sebastian has been a guest lecturer at University College London Medical School (where he studied Medicine) and University College London Institute of Education speaking on emotional intelligence, kindness, compassion, resilience and leadership to trainee doctors and teachers. His expertise has led to speaking invitations from universities across the world including Stanford, Rutgers, and the University of California, Berkeley in the USA, the University of Buenos Aires Medical School and the University of Espirito Santo in Brazil and Hong Kong Polytechnic University.

Sebastian is currently a doctoral researcher in the Management Department at Birkbeck College, University of London focusing on the role of kindness in leadership and organisational performance. Prior to this he led a yearlong research collaboration between Cambridge University and University College London Institute of Education on academic performance and wellbeing.

Sebastian holds qualifications in medical science, management, teaching, educational psychological assessment and educational neuroscience. He is an alumnus of Imperial College London, Bristol University, London Metropolitan University, Middlesex University, Birkbeck College and University College London.

Born in London to a French mother and Argentine father, Sebastian has lived most of his life in London except for a year in Germany and shorter six-month and three-month working stays in Argentina, the USA and China. He speaks French, Spanish and German and is currently learning Japanese and Mandarin.

Index

Kindness is not just "nice", it's necessary for success.

Sebastian offers keynotes, talks and training on how kindness improves outcomes and why therefore we need to prioritise it.

Whether you need leadership development for senior executives, wellbeing and resilience training for managers, cultural integration training following a merger or acquisition, or customer service training for front-line staff, prioritising kindness is critical to success. Participants gain a uniquely powerful new knowledge base and skillset grounded in scientific research that fuels their growth, development and performance. The current list of trainings that apply the science of kindness to improve outcomes include:

- Resilience in Times of Challenge
- Effective Leadership
- Enhanced Wellbeing
- Performing Under Pressure
- Excellence in Healthcare
- Enhancing Team Performance
- Excelling at Customer Service
- Enhanced Cross-Cultural Management
- Improved Learning & Creativity
- Enhanced Safety in High-Risks Environments
- Enhancing Brand Value
- Improved and learning and wellbeing for exam success
- The Science of Kindness

Client Feedback includes:

"This was a massively helpful afternoon of training. I'm going to implement some of the techniques as of tomorrow! The presention was great. Really, clear friendly and the right mix of theory and practice. 10/10." Course Participant. Trainee teacher, Institute of Education, University College London.

"Thank you for running such a fantastic interactive seminar on compassionate care for all our directors and senior managers. Colleagues have commented how informative and thought-provoking session had been. We appreciate your expertise and ability to deliver the talk in Spanish! Thank you so much." Soledad Rodriguez Casanova, Director of HR Diaverum, Argentina.

"I would definitely recommend Sebastian's talks on kindness in the workplace. Sebastian passion and enthusiasm to encourage collective kindness comes through clearly and is so needed across the professional sectors". Gina Antwi, Senior Appointment Advisor, UK Department of international Trade.

I would highly recommend Sebastian's talks on kindness in the workplace as he gave an extremely informative talk at our office in Edinburgh. Everyone enjoyed the content, and it was good to re-enforce behaviours which are often forgotten during periods of stress. Rachel Miller, Digital Analyst, Accenture.

Thank you for doing such a fabulous presentation. It was a real success. You timed it really well, interacted excellently with attendees and the slides were great. Taylor Damiani, International Positive Pshychology Association.

Contact Sebastian today for training and speaking engagements

hello@kindness-advantage.com
+44 7540135189

Printed in Great Britain
by Amazon

70624623R00085